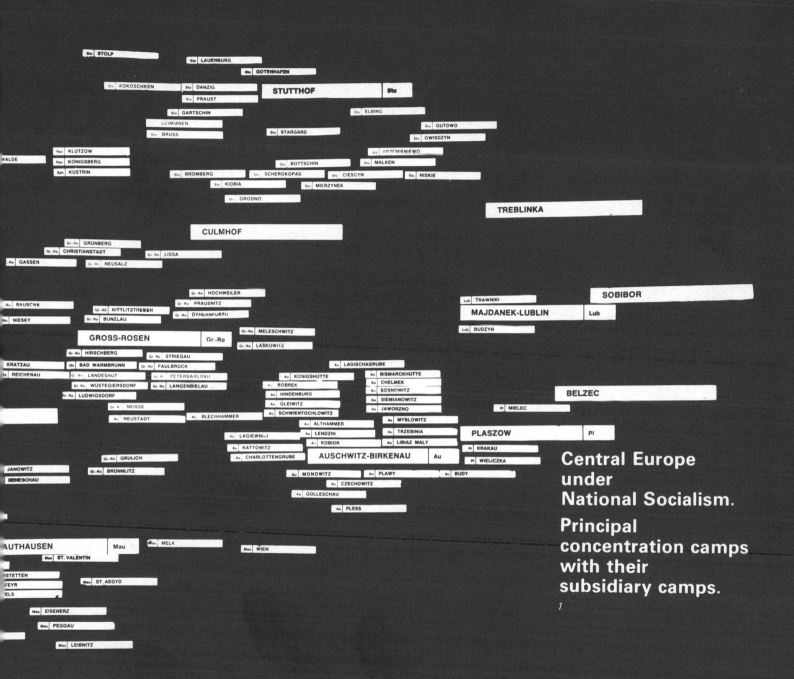

Central Europe under National Socialism.

Principal concentration camps with their subsidiary camps.

1

This museum was opened on May 9, 1965.
It was constructed by the Bavarian State
on the initiative and according to the plans
of the International Dachau Committee.

ISBN 3-87490-528-4

17. Edition

Catalogue	© 1978
Publishers	Comité International de Dachau, Brussels Lipp GmbH, Munich
Editors	Barbara Distel, Ruth Jakusch
Translation	Jennifer Vernon, in cooperation with: Ruth Jakusch, Barbara Distel

CONCENTRATION CAMP DACHAU

1933 — 1945

Introduction

This catalogue is intended to accompany the visitor to the Dachau Memorial Museum through the exhibition and to provide him with a reference guide to all the documents displayed.

On the basis of currently available material, an attempt is made to present the history of the Dachau concentration camp from 1933 until 1945, to show how it came into being and how it was developed during the Nazi era, firstly as a training centre, and then as a model camp for the SS in the perfection of the inhuman concentration camp system, a training ground for the extermination camps of Auschwitz, Majdanek, Treblinka etc.

Although Dachau was not intended as a "mass extermination camp", hunger and illness, arbitrary killings and mass executions along with the SS doctors' pseudo-scientific experiments, resulted in the continual "extermination" of prisoners. In addition, more than 3000 sick and handicapped Dachau prisoners were murdered in the gas chambers of the Hartheim euthanasia institution near Linz. Many more, especially Jewish prisoners, were transferred to extermination camps.

As early as March 21, 1933, Heinrich Himmler, then Police Commissioner of Munich, announced to the press that the first concentration camp for Communist and Social Democratic functionnaries was to be opened on March 22 in Dachau.

Originally planned to accomodate 5000 prisoners, the camp was primarily intended to eliminate all political opposition. In the course of time, in addition to Jews, gypsies and anti-Nazi clergymen, any citizens who made themselves unpopular with the regime were imprisoned here.

An attempt was made to discriminate against these political detainees by introducing common criminals, homosexuals and so called "antisocials" into the concentration camp. In 1937, owing to continuously increasing numbers, prison labour was used to enlarge the camp.

The ratio of the various nationalities between 1939 and 1945 reflected the course of the war. As soon as the German army had invaded a country, the first prisoner transports began to arrive. In these occupied countries the Germans tried to stifle all opposition by deporting all intellectual and political leaders. Jewish citizens were persecuted everywhere. Deportation was greatly accelerated during the last years of the war, as it provided the basis of the slave labour force necessary for the German armaments industry.

On April 29, 1945, the liberators of the Dachau camp found more than 30000 survivors of 31 different nationalities*) in the disastrously overcrowded barracks, and as many again in subsidiary camps attached to Dachau.

During its 12 years of existence, 206000 prisoners were registered in Dachau. The number of "non-registered" arrivals can no longer be ascertained.

During this period of time 31.951 deaths were registered. However, the total number of deaths in Dachau, including the victims of individual and mass executions and the final death marches will never be known.

Before the liberation of the camp the Comité International de Dachau was secretly constituted, its aim being to prevent the last-minute mass extermination of the prisoners planned by the SS.

During the weeks after the liberation, the committee played an important role in providing for the survivors taking care of the sick, and finally in organizing the repatriation of released prisoners.

Members of the SS captured by the US Army were then held in custody in the Dachau camp until the end of the Dachau war crimes trials. Afterwards, refugees and displaced persons were housed in these barracks,**) some for as long as 18 years, until they were offered adequate housing accommodation.

The first International meeting of former Dachau prisoners took place in 1955, on the 10th anniversary of the camp's liberation. In view of the deteriorating condition of the camp, it was unanimously decided to re-establish the Comité International de Dachau in order to insist on behalf of all ex-prisoners that a worthy and dignified memorial be set up.

In 1960, a provisional museum was opened in the crematorium building as a first result of these joint efforts. Finally, on May 9, 1965, the opening ceremony of the present memorial site and museum took place. The Comité International de Dachau was responsible for its concept and planing and the Bavarian Government for its financing. Consulting architect René Vander Auwera, former Dachau prisoner No. 113087.

Attached to the museum are cinema, archives and a specialist library.

Appendix

It must be emphasized that this documentation is based only on documents still accessible.

Many incidents are no longer verifiable, as shortly before the liberation the SS destroyed a substantial part of the records that were incriminating to them.

In such a documentation it is almost impossible to portray acts of resistance and solidarity among the prisoners themselves, as, apart from prisoners' correspondence with their families (which was of course strictly censored), there exists no written evidence relating to their camp experiences.

The documents on display, which originated during the Nazi era, voice the spirit of the Nazi State: vocabulary and expressions used are typical of Nazi terminology.

Photographs of other concentration camps displayed in the museum which are also applicable to the history of Dachau are always acknowledged as such.

Provision has been made for future additions to the documentation as new material and information becomes available.

*) According to a list of nationalities found among SS documents. In accordance with Nazi terminology, countries such as Latvia and the Ukraine were classified as separate states, whereas Austria was regarded as part of the German Reich. By present day classifications, there were prisoners from 27 different countries interned in Dachau. There is a commemorative plaque for each of these countries in the entrance hall of the museum.

**) At the time of the setting up of the memorial site, all the barrack buildings were derelict and therefore had to be demolished. Two of the huts were then reconstructed, of the others only the foundations were left.

Taken from the documentation displayed, terms which are no longer used:

Baracke "X"	Euphemism for crematorium
Block	Barrack hut
Capo	Prisoners' foreman
Fememord	1929–1933 numerous political murders were comitted on the orders of secret political tribunals
"Final Solution of the Jewish Question"	Euphemism for the methodical extermination of European Jewry
Gestapo	Secret State Police
Hunger Oedema	Dropsy – result of malnutrition
"Invalid transports"	Over 3000 so-called "invalid prisoners" were sent from Dachau concentration camp to Hartheim Castle where they were gassed.
"Jourhaus"	Guard house, camp entrance
"Muselmann"	Prisoner who was completely exhausted and emaciated.
NN (Nacht und Nebel)	lit. Night and Fog (s. exhibit no. 373)
NSDAP	National Socialist Workers' Party
PG (Parteigenosse)	Party member
Phlegmone	Festering sores due to malnutrition
Political Coordination	enforced standardization in conformity with NS doctrine
Political Department	Branch of the Gestapo in the concentration camps, independent of the camp administration.
Protective Custody	Imprisonment of political opponents made possible by the emergency regulation of February 28, 1933

Reichsbanner	Self-defence organization of the Social Democratic Party during the Weimar Republic
RSHA (Reichssicherheitshauptamt)	The Central Security Department of the Reich formed in 1937, combining the existing police (Gestapo and criminal police) and the Security Service (SD).
RF SS (Reichsführer SS)	Chief of the SS and the German Police Heinrich Himmler's full title from 1936.
Roll-call	The roll-call took place every morning and evening. The prisoners were often made to stand for hours on end in the roll call square in all weathers and inadequately clothed.
SA (Sturmabteilung)	The Stormtroopers (brownshirts) of the Nazi Party
"Shot whilst escaping"	Excuse for shooting prisoners
Special treatment ("Sonderbehandlung")	Euphemism for execution
SS (Schutzstaffel)	Originally an elite military formation of the Nazi Party, a unit of which was later put in charge of the concentration camps ("Totenkopfverbände" = Death's head Units).
SS WVHA (SS-Wirtschaftsverwaltungshauptamt)	SS Head Office for economic organization. It controlled the economic enterprises of the SS and administered the concentration camps.
Volksgenosse	Nazi term for compatriot

Contents

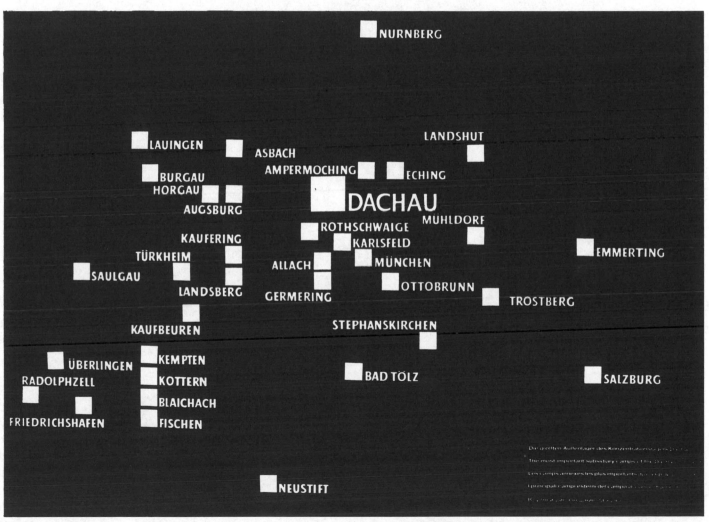

3   The most important subsidiary camps of the Dachau concentration camp

Belgique   Bŭlgarija

        Československo   Danmark

Deutschland   ΕΛΛΑΣ

        España   France

Great-Britain   ישׂראד כ

        Italia   Jugoslavija

Luxembourg   Magyarország

Nederland

Norge

Österreich

Polska

Portugal

România

Schweiz

Shqipëri

Suomi

CCCP

Sverige

Türkiye

USA

Historical background to the "Third Reich"

Intensified nationalism
and anti-semitism
encourage its development

National Socialism emerges,
establishes itself
and then seizes power

Verſuch

über die

Ungleichheit der Menſchenracen.

Vom

Grafen Gobineau.

Deutſche Ausgabe

von

Ludwig Schemann.

Zweiter Band.

Vierte Auflage.

Stuttgart.
Fr. Frommanns Verlag (H. Kurtz)
1922

5   Essay on the Dissimilarity of the Human Race
by Count Gobineau
German Edition by Ludwig Schemann
Second Volume, Fourth Edition
Stuttgart, F. Frommans Publishers (H. Kurtz), 1922

The Germanic Aryans
Retrospect. Characteristics of the three great races in their relation to one another; social effects of their combination; the superiority of the white race and before all the Aryan family.

Only the white nations have a history. Why nearly all civilizations have developed in the Occident.

written 1853–1855

Houston Stewart Chamberlain

DIE
GRUNDLAGEN
DES NEUNZEHNTEN
JAHRHUNDERTS

◆

ZWEITE HÄLFTE

◆

*Wir bekennen uns zu dem Geschlecht,
das aus dem Dunkeln ins Helle strebt.*
Goethe

XIV. AUFLAGE

MÜNCHEN 1922 / BEI F. BRUCKMANN A.-G.

Houston Stewart Chamberlain,
The Foundation of the Nineteenth Century
Second Half
We believe in the species which struggles out of the darkness into the light.   Goethe
XIV Edition
Munich 1922, F. Bruckmann AG, Publishers

Scientific Confusion p.285—The Meaning of Race p.295—the Five Basic Principles   p.300—Other Influences   p.314—The   Nation p.316—The Hero p.321—Chaos where there is no Racial Distinction p.323—Lucian p.326—Augustinus p. 332—Ascetic Delusion p.336—The Sacredness of a pure Race p.339—Germanic Peoples p.342.

Chapter Five: the Appearance of the Jews in Occidental (Western) History.

The Jewish Question p.353—The "Foreign" People p. 360—Historical Bird's-Eye View p.364—Consensus ingeniorum p.367—Princes and Aristocracy p.370—Internal Contact p.373—Who are the Jews? p.375—
Classification of the Investigation p.378—The Origin of the Israelites p.381—The Genuine Semite p.388—The Syrian p.391—The Amorite p.401—Comparative Figures p.405—Racial Guilt Feelings p.408—Homo   Syriacus   p.411—Homo   Europacus   p.414—Homo Arabicus p.415—Homo Judaeus p.425—A Discourse about the Semitic Religion p.428—Israel and Judea p.456—The Coming of the Jews p.462—The New Alliance p.477—The Prophets p.479—The Rabbies p.485—Messianism p.489—The Law p.495—The Thora p.498—Judaism p.500.

6

A fundamental characteristic of the new "Teutonentum" was an inveterate hatred of the Jews. The violent excitement generated by the war of liberation brought to light all the secrets of this German feeling, and so in this atmosphere of general unrest the old, deep-rooted resentment towards anything oriental came once more to the fore.

The poets of the great national struggle sang the praises of the war – the sole artistic activity which was at once politically acceptable. Their patriotic enthusiasm awakened eternal, purely human emotions, a cry to arms, fighting instinct and the hope and joy of victory. They pursued a specific, clearly recognizable goal – the liberation of the "Fatherland" from foreign oppressors.

7

Heinrich v. Treitschke: German History (1879)

8

Chapter Six: The Appearance of the Germanic Peoples in World History.

Chapter Nine: From the year 1200 until the year 1800.

1. Discovery (from Marco Polo to Galvani)

First Edition 1899

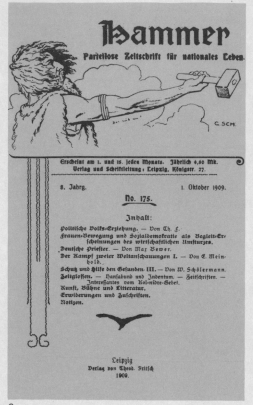

9

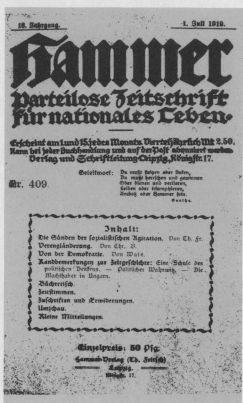

10

11

HAMMER

Independent Periodical for National Life

Appears on the 1st and the 15th of each month. Annual Subscription 6,60 Mk. Publishers and Editors—Leipzig, Königstr. 27 8th Year of Publication, 1st October, 1909 No. 175

Contents:

People's Political Education—by Th. F. The Suffragette Movement and Social Democracy, the Symptoms of Economic Downfall German Priests—by Max Bever. The Struggle between two Ideologies—by E. Meinhold. Protection and Help for the Healthy—by W. Schölermann. Today's Glossary—"Hansabund" and Jewry—Periodicals Interesting Aspects of the Kol-Nidre Prayer Art, Theatre and Literature Notes

Leipzig
Theodor Fritsch Publishers
1909

18th Year of Publication   July 1, 1919
HAMMER

Independent Periodical for National Life Appears on the 1st and the 15th of each month Quarterly Subscription 2,50 Mk. Subscription at any booksellers or post office. Publishers and Editors—Leipzig, Königstr. 17 No. 409

Geleitwort: Goethe

Contents:

The Faults of Socialist Agitation—by Th. Fr. Anglicisation—by Chr. B. About Democracy—by Wate. Marginal Notes on Contemporary History: A School of political Reasoning—Political Insanity—The Rulers in Hungary. The Bookstall Contemporary Comments. Letters to the Editor und Answers. Review Information

Prize: 50 Pfg.
Hammer Publishers (Th. Fritsch)
Leipzig, Königstr. 17

HAMMER

Journal for the German Mind
Editor: Theodor Fritsch

Contents:

Karl Peters and his People .... Theodor Fritsch
The Declining Birth Rate,
A German Problem
of Fundamental Importance .... Paul Erich Petzold
Rise and Fall of
Nations and Cultures .... Kurt Gerlach
On Domestic Policy .... Munin
About Ousting Rationalism through
Traditionalism in the
Educational Field .... Josef Stibitz
Talmud Morals .... The Rev. Falck

Marginal Notes on Contemporary History: Big Finance and Politics—The "Tribute" Problem—The Dangers of Department Stores—Who is the busybody at Frankfurt University, dealing with "Psycho Analysis"—Hugenberg's America Letter—

The Bookstall—Letters to the Editor—Information

Prize 50 Pfg
28th Year of Publication—April 15, 1920—No. 644 Hammer—Publishers—Leipzig C 1

12

ARE YOU BLOND?
Are you fed up with the mob administration?
Then read "Ostara", Publications for blondes and the male rights movement!
No. 71
Race and Aristocracy

13

ARE YOU BLOND?
Then you create and safeguard culture!
You should therefore read "Ostara", Publications for blondes and the male rights movement!
No. 72
Race and Foreign Politics

14

ARE YOU BLOND?
Then you are in danger! You should therefore read "Ostara", Publications for blondes and the male rights movement
No. 73
Blondes are the creators of music!

15

Anti-semitic postcard from Borkum, a well-known spa, from the turn of the century.

10. Als Thiers die Welschen aufgerührt hatte.

1. Und brauset der Sturmwind des Krieges heran,
Und wollen die Welschen ihn haben,
So sammle, mein Deutschland, dich stark wie ein Mann
Und bringe die blutigen Gaben
Und bringe das Schrecken und trage das Grauen
Von all deinen Bergen, aus all deinen Gauen
Und klinge die Losung: „Zum Rhein! übern Rhein!
Alldeutschland in Frankreich hinein!"

2. Sie wollen's: so reiße denn, deutsche Geduld
Reiß' durch von dem Belt bis zum Rheine!
Wir fordern die lange gestundete Schuld —
Auf, Welsche, und rühret die Beine!
Wir wollen im Spiele der Schwerter und Lanzen
Den wilden, den blutigen Tanz mit euch tanzen,
Wir klingen die Losung: „Zum Rhein! übern Rhein!
Alldeutschland in Frankreich hinein!"

3. Mein einziges Deutschland, mein kühnes, heran!
Wir wollen ein Liedlein euch singen
Von dem, was die schleichende List euch gewann,
Von Straßburg und Metz und Lothringen:
Zurück sollt ihr zahlen, heraus sollt ihr geben!
So stehe der Kampf uns auf Tod und auf Leben!
So klinge die Losung: „Zum Rhein! übern Rhein!
Alldeutschland in Frankreich hinein!"

4. Mein einiges Deutschland, mein freies, heran!
Sie wollen, sie sollen es haben.
Auf! sammle und rüste dich stark wie ein Mann
Und bringe die blutigen Gaben!
Du, das sie nun nimmer mit Listen zersplittern,
Erbrause wie Windsbraut aus schwarzen Gewittern!
So klinge die Losung: „Zum Rhein! übern Rhein!
Alldeutschland in Frankreich hinein!"

(1841.)

16
German reader from 1911

A chauvinist poem with the refrain "To the Rhine, across the Rhine! Germany forward into France!" (1841)

A branch of a Germanic Order founded in Northern Germany in 1912 was set up in Munich in 1918.

In the summer of 1918 the Munich branch established its offices in the "Vier Jahreszeiten" Hotel and camouflaged itself as the "Thule Society". The Germanic Order was a secret anti-semitic lodge, organized on the lines of the Freemasons. Their principles were: "Only at least third generation pure blooded Germans are eligible for membership; great value is to be placed on the propagation of racial information; the principles of the "Alldeutsche" are to be extended to the entire German Race. Everything non-German must be fought against." Julius Streicher, Rudolf Hess, Alfred Rosenberg, Gottfried Feder, Dietrich Eckhart and Hans Frank belonged to this "Thule Society" circle.
One member, Karl Harrer, formed a workers' group within the organisation itself to take care of the interests of nationalistic workers.

The foundation of the German Workers' Party followed on January 5, 1919, Harrer having contributed to the initial planning.

On Sept. 12, 1919 Captain Mayr, a member of the staff of the Reichswehrgruppenkommando IV, sent a confidential agent to one of their meetings. His name was Adolf Hitler.

"Origin and Nature of National Socialism", by Helga Grebing

17

Poster 1915   18

19 ''The Supreme Military Command maintains its demand for the immediate offer of a peace treaty to the enemy.

The weakening of our western reserves, a result of the collapse of the Macedonian front, has made it impossible to repair the very considerable losses incurred during the most recent confrontations. In view of this, we can no longer hope to dictate a peace settlement to our enemies.

Furthermore, the enemy is constantly re-inforcing his front lines with fresh reinforcements.

At the moment the German Forces are still in a position to hold their ground and are successfully repelling all attacks. However, the situation, which is worsening daily, could force the Supreme Military Command into making some very far-reaching decisions.

Under these circumstances the struggle ought to be ended in order to avoid senseless loss of life to the German people and their Allies. Each day lost costs the lives of countless brave soldiers.''

signed von Hindenburg

Ludendorff, My War Memoirs 1914–1918

18
Death and danger in bloody battle
Wind and weather in solitary vigil
God shall take care of us — you beloved ones at home.
Hope and pray, we'll never yield!

Hamburg's day of sacrifice — November 1
Christmas Donation 1915

20

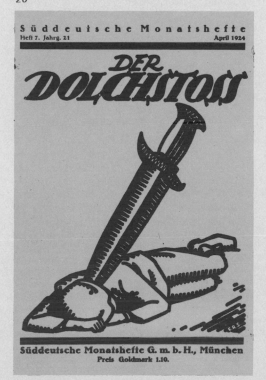

21
It was obvious to the Supreme Military Command several months before the end of the war, that, in military terms, Germany was already defeated. To avoid admission of this fact later, they spread the ''Dolchstoss''* legend in which they claimed that the army had in fact had real chances of winning the war, but that the fighting spirit had been broken by socialist subversive activities. Hindenburg confirmed this version before a Governmental committee of inquiry. This lie was an insult to the Republic and played an important role in its eventual downfall.

* (stab in the back)

Deutsche-Arbeiter-Partei
Ortsgruppe München
München, den 2. Dezember 1919

Wir ersuchen Sie hiermit zu der am Mittwoch.10.Dez. 1919
abends punkt 7 Uhr im groessen Saale des Gasthauses

„ zum Deutschen Reich "

Dachauerstr.143 (bei Haltestelle Loristr. Linie 24) stattfindenden

Versammlung

bestimmt zu erscheinen

Redner: Herr H i t l e r über

„ Deutschland vor seiner tiefsten Erniedrigung "

Die Einladung dient als Ausweis. Der Saal ist geheizt.

Der Ausschuß

1.A. Josef Mayer
1.Schriftführer
Andräßtr. 10/3 S.B

24
Poster 1920

22

GERMAN WORKERS' PARTY

Munich Branch
Munich, December 2, 1919

Your presence is hereby requested on Wednesday, December 10, 1919, in the large assembly hall of the "Zum Deutschen Reich", Dachauerstr. 143 (next to the tram stop, Loristr. No. 24) where a
MEETING
is to be held.
Speaker: Mr. Hitler on
"Germany facing its worst humiliation." This invitation will ensure entrance. The hall is heated.

The Committee
Joseph Mayr
First secretary
Andrästr. 10/3

23

3. We demand the requisition of territories (colonies) to provide food for our people and for the resettlement of our surplus population.

4. Only compatriots ("Volksgenossen") may be citizens. Regardless of his confession, a compatriot must be of German blood. Jews are therefore excluded from this status.

8. Any further immigration of non-Germans is to be stopped. We demand that all non-Germans who have immigrated since August 2, 1914, shall be forced to leave the Reich immediately.
Munich, February 24, 1920

Extract from the program of the NSDAP (German National Socialist Workers' Party)

National Socialist
GERMAN WORKERS' PARTY
ALL

people tell us: Your programme appears to be correct but one point prevents us from joining you and that is we don't understand your OPPOSITION TO THE JEWS. Are there not also good Jews and, vice versa CHRISTIAN SCOUNDRELS? Aren't you aware of the Christian profiteers, blackmarketeers, exploiters, capitalists and their press? Can the Jews be blamed if they are not German? We will explain to you: We fight all kinds of capital, Jewish or German, which is only used to earn interest, an income without labour or effort. We fight the Jews, not because they are the sole owners of such capital, but because they are the founders of this system and they deliberately hinder any opposition to it. We fight them not because they are the only profiteers but because their one percent of the entire population represents 90 percent of all profiteers. We fight them not because they are the only gluttons in our present time of need, but because their one percent of the population includes 90 percent of all gluttons. But above all, we fight them because of their ability to appear innocent whilst allowing others to take the blame for their deeds. Those who cause millions of small hoarders to be hunted as CHRISTIAN RACKETEERS so that they themselves can safely make millions on the black market. Above all we fight them because they only support a law so long as they themselves are not directly affected, but as soon as it is applied to criminals of their own race it becomes JEW-BAITING. We fight them as a foreign race not because they are non-German but because they fraudulently pretend to be German. We fight them because, as Mommsen says, they are "enzymes of destruction" to countries and races. Whilst destroying countries and driving starving people to emigrate to strange lands they, themselves strangers, settle in these countries. We fight their actions as they cause a RACIAL TUBERCULOSIS OF NATIONS. And we are convinced that convalescence can only begin when this bacteria has been removed. This is why we appeal to you ALL to attend the big public MEETING TODAY, FRIDAY August 13, in the Hofbräuhaus (Platzl). Adolf Hitler will speak about: WHY ARE WE ANTISEMITICS? The meeting begins at 7.30 p.m. Listen to us first and then decide! An etrance fee of 50 Pfennigs will be charged to cover expenses.

For the Party: Anton Drächsler

25 Poster 1918

DECLARATION

by the New Chancellor of the Reich *Ebert*

APPEAL FOR PEACE AND ORDER

Citizens! The former Chancellor of the Reich, Prinz Max von Bayern, together with all the Secretaries of State, has entrusted me with the responsibility of Chancellor of the Reich. With the consent of the political parties I am in the process of forming a new government, which will shortly be made public. The new government, will be a peoples' government. Its first priority must be to bring peace to the German People and then to stabilize the newly achieved freedom. Citizens! I ask you all for your support in the difficult task which awaits us. You know that war severely threatens the nation's food reserves, a fundamental guarantee for political stability. The political upheaval should not be allowed to disrupt food distribution to the population. The promotion of food production and food distribution to the towns should not be hindered, it must remain the most important duty of everyone, both in the towns and in the country. A food shortage means looting, want and misery for everyone. The poor would suffer most, and the industrial workers would be the worst affected. Those who misappropriate food and other necessary commodities or the means of transport for their distribution, commit a severe crime against the entire population. Citizens! I beg you all most urgently to clear the streets and to ensure pease and order.

Berlin, November 9, 1918   The Chancellor of the Reich
                                                                                  Ebert

28

Members of the "Ehrhardt Brigade", alreadey wearing the swastika emblem at the time of the "Kapp-Putsch" in March 1920

MINISTRY OF THE REICH — PROCLAMATION

Kapp and Lüttwitz have resigned.
The criminal adventure in Berlin is over.
The struggle of the last few days has proved irrefutably to the whole world that democracy in Germany is not an illusion but that it is the only power capable of dealing with a military dictatorship in no time.

The rebuilding of the State and economy, which was criminally interrupted, must be continued until success is achieved. To achieve it, the labour force must refrain from making use of its very powerful weapon, the General Strike.

The Government will do all in its power to encourage reconstruction and will severely punish the traitors who forced you into a general strike. We will make sure that a horde of soldiers will never again be able to interfere with the People's destiny. We have achieved victory together! To work!

The President of the Reich   The Government of the Reich
Ebert   Bauer

26 Poster 1920

27
The Free Corps of Werdenfels, a nationalistic military organization, later one of the main supporters of the "Hitler-Putsch"
(the attempt by Hitler and his followers to come to power in
1922)

29   The so-called "German Day"
                                              Nuremberg, 1923

Proklamation
an das deutsche Volk!
Die Regierung der November-
verbrecher in Berlin ist heute für
abgesetzt erklärt worden.
Eine
**provisorische deutsche
Nationalregierung**
ist gebildet worden, diese besteht aus
**Gen. Ludendorff
Ad. Hitler, Gen. v. Lossow
Obst. v. Seisser**

II/25

PROCLAMATION to the German People!
Today the Government of the "November Conspirators" has
been dismissed.
A provisional National German Government has been
formed, consisting of
Gen. Ludendorff
Ad. Hitler, Gen. v. Lossow
Col. v. Seisser

30
November 1923

31

The "Hitler Putsch", November 1923
SA-men at the Marienplatz.

32

On the 9th of November, 1923, Hitler and Ludendorff along with their supporters tried to occupy the Munich Ministries in an attempt to instigate an uprising. The Generalstaatskommissar Gustav von Kahr and the Reichswehrgeneral von Lossow, who had initially toyed with the idea of a Putsch, withdrew their support at the last moment and alarmed the army and police, whose firing halted the march of the insurgents in front of the Feldherrnhalle. Sixteen people were killed and Hitler was arrested. In spring 1924, he was sentenced to five years' imprisonment (minimum sentence) and released on parole in December 1924. Ludendorff was acquitted.

33

The accused in the "Hitler trial"

34

Münchner Neueste Nachrichten
April 2, 1924
Grounds for the verdict in the Hitler trial
". . . Also, the court is convinced that the accused were guided in their actions by a purely patriotic spirit and a most noble and selfless determination."

CATEGORIES OF POLITICAL MURDER

"Fatally injured"	184	Shot in reprisal	10
Arbitrary shooting	73	Arbitrary shooting	8
"Shot whilst escaping"	45	Alleged martial law	3
Alleged martial law	37	Alleged self-defence	1
Alleged self-defence	9		
Lynched in prison or during transport	5		
Alleged suicide	1		
Total of victims murdered by right-wing supporters	354	Total of victims murdered by left-wing supporters	22

SENTENCES FOR THE POLITICAL MURDERS

	Political murders committed by		total
	left-wing supporters	right-wing supporters	
Total of murders	22	354	376
not prosecuted	4	326	330
sentences partly served	1	27	28
sentences fully served	17	1	18
Number of convictions	38	24	
Acquittal of those who acknowledged their deed	—	23	
Promotion for those who acknowledged their deed	—	3	
Duration of prison sentence per murder	15 years	4 mths	
Number of executions	10	—	
Fine per murder	—	2 marks	

E. Gumbel "Four years of political murder" 1922

(This organisation succeeded the "Ehrhardt Brigade" and was responsible for the assassination of the democratic politicians Erzberger and Rathenau and the attempts on the lives of Scheidemann and Harden.)

A. a) To encourage and foster the propagation of patriotic ideals.
   b) Fight everything anti- and international, Jewry, Social Democrats and the radical left-wing parties.
   c) Fight the anti-national Weimar Constitution, both in the spoken and written word.
§ 1   It is a secret organisation, known as "Organisation C"
§ 7   Jews and all people of foreign races are not eligible for membership.
§ 11   Traitors will be dealt with by the "Feme."
§ 12   The oath of allegiance is as follows: "I declare on my honour that I am of German descent. I subject myself to the laws of the O.C. and pledge this allegiance on my word of honour. I vow obedience to the leader of the organisation and to my superiors. I shall observe absolute secrecy in all matters concerning the organisation, even after eventual resignation.
Our Slogan: Fight for Germany's rebirth.

36
Extract from the charter of the "Fememord — Organisation Consul"

German Reader 1926   *38*

PREFACE

During this time of national need it is becoming generally acknowledged that all hope for our Fatherland depends upon the education of our youth towards a self-sacrificing love for their home and Fatherland. This is the aim of our new reader, the first volume of which is suitable for the first two elementary school classes. It is not intended to be an arbitrary collection of interesting and instructive information, as is usually the case with school readers, but as a guide to things German, to the beauty of our homeland, the understandig of German labour, pride in the great achievments of our people — both past and present — a respect for all ''Volksgenossen'', whether finely dressed or in working clothes, the recognition of the special nature of German life and character, and a respect for the German heritage. All that the spirit of our people has produced in songs and sagas, in light-heartedness and seriousness, everything beautiful and gentle, everything good and courageous, that which lies within German national life and bursts forth out of the fresh springs of German poetry should be the child's friend and companion, an introduction to the riches of the German character which will open his eyes to the whole of what he himself will one day take part in creating.

37

Free from Versailles!
Away from the Jewish Social Front!
For Freedom and the Fatherland!
Your Motto: National German!

Poster 1924

39 Nationalistic poem gloryfying the German fighting spirit.

40
Field Marshal Paul von Hindenburg becomes President of the Weimar Republic.

41
1931, Meeting of the right-wing nationalist ex-servicemen's "Stahlhelm" organization.

Münchner Neueste Nachrichten

No. 262 Friday, September 26, 1930, p.5

"Hitler as witness before the Reichs' Court"

Leipzig, September 25th

Today's hearing in the Reichswehr trial attracted great interest because of the interrogation of the National Socialist party leader, Adolf Hitler.

The chairman read out an article in which is stated amongst other things that "Hitler makes no attempt to disguise the gravity of the struggle. He says: heads will roll in this struggle, either theirs or ours, so we must ensure that it will be theirs."
The chairman continued: This can be interpreted as a wish for a revolution. Can you qualify this quotation?
Hitler: I believe that the author Muchow was referring to the great spiritual revolution in which we find ourselves today. There will be a "Staatsgerichtshof" when the movement has won its legar struggle. Atonement will be had for November 1918 and heads will roll.

(in the same issue) London, September 25
The London evening press reports about today's trial at great length. In the headlines one reads of heads which will roll in the sand.

42

Poster 1931   43

GERMANS! BUY GERMAN PRODUCTS

GERMAN WEEK
GERMAN PRODUCTS
GERMAN LABOUR

44   Poster 1930

Compatriots! We are beating them to pieces! Help us to beat them down! Parliament is creaking at its joints. We are going to shake it until it breaks apart! Come along to the great rallies of the National Socialist Movement. Every single man and woman of you to our meetings! In the Marsfeld circus building on

Friday Sept.5 Dr. Goebbels, the leader of the German city of
8 p.m.   Berlin ''THE THIRD REICH — THE STATE OF THE
                WORKER, THE BRAIN AND THE FIST''

Saturday Sept. 13
8 p.m.   Our final blow!

Sunday Sept. 14, 1930! Help us to smash the system! Vote for list 9: National Socialist German Workers' Party of Munich—Adolf Wagner

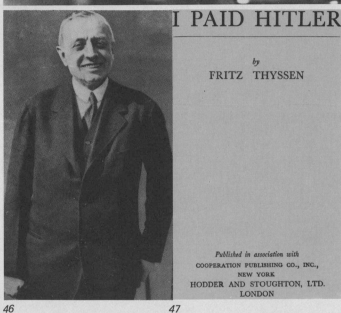

1931, National-Socialists, German-Nationalists and the "Stahlhelm" — all hostile to the Republic — unite and found the "Harzburger Front"

48

"It is common knowledge that on January 27th, 1932 — almost a year before he seized power — Adolf Hitler made a speech lasting about two and a half hours before the Industry Club of Düsseldorf. The speech made a deep impression on the assembled industrialists, and in consequence of this a number of large contributions flowed from the resources of heavy industry into the treasuries of the National Socialist party."

Fritz Thyssen emigrated in 1939 at the outbreak of the war and openly turned against National Socialism.
Upon the initiative of the German authorities he was arrested in France, 1941, and taken to Germany where he spent the remaining war years in various penal institutions and prison camps.

I PAID HITLER

by

FRITZ THYSSEN

Published in association with
COOPERATION PUBLISHING CO., INC.,
NEW YORK
HODDER AND STOUGHTON, LTD.
LONDON

46   **47**

49

In 1932 Hitler is received by leading representatives of heavy industry.

50

Six million unemployed at the beginning of 1932

More Power for the President of the Reich
Away with Parliament's exclusive Sovereignty
(Article 54)
Vote German National

51
"Hitler, a German destiny",
1932 by A. Paul Weber

52
Poster 1932

53
Seizure of Power on 30 January, 1933

54
Hitler, Vice Chancellor von Papen (conservative monarchist) and von Blomberg, Minister for the "Reichswehr" (German Armed Forces)

ER MARSCHALL UND DER GEFREITE

KÄMPFEN MIT UNS FÜR FRIEDEN UND GLEICHBERECHTIGUNG

55
The Field Marshall and the Corporal fight with us for Freedom and Equality

56
Some of the first arrests

BE ON YOUR GUARD!

On January 30, 1933, Adolf Hitler, the leader of the German freedom movement, was made Chancellor of the German Reich. On March 5, the German people, whole-heartedly acknowledged their support for him and his endeavours. The

NATIONAL REVOLUTION

has smashed the old system to the ground. Marxism lies shattered, Germany faces a new prosperity. This great German struggle for liberation fills

INTERNATIONAL JEWRY

with hatred and rage. They see their power in Germany coming to an end. They see that they can no longer make Germany into a Soviet Jewish criminal colony. Now they are acting in accordance with the programme of the Jewish Zionist leader, Theodor Herzl, which was solemnly proclaimed at the Jewish congress in Basel in 1897 (extract from the 7th meeting):

''As soon as a non-Jewish State dares to oppose us we must be in a position to provoke its neighbours into declaring war against it. We will then use public opinion as a pretext.''

At the moment the Jews are putting an extensive plan into action to stir up world opinion against Germany. Using the press, they are spreading a monstrous flood of lies throughout the world. No crime, no disgrace is too base for them. They accuse the Germans.

THE JEWS ARE LYING .In Germany, members of the Jewish race are supposedly being brutally tortured to death.

THE JEWS ARE LYING Their eyes being gouged out, their hands hacked off, their ears and noses cut off, and even their corpses dismembered.

THE JEWS ARE LYING Allegedly, not even Jewish women are spared from such gruesome deaths and young Jewish girls are raped in front of their parents.

These lies are being propagated in the same way and to the same ends as they were during the war — in order to incite world opinion against Germany.

In addition to this a

BOYCOTT OF GERMAN GOODS

is being demanded. By this they are seeking to increase poverty and unemployment in Germany, and to ruin the German export trade. German men and women! The culprits in this absurd crime, in this vile smear and boycott campaign are the

JEWS IN GERMANY

They have appealed to their racial brethren abroad to fight against Germany. They have spread their slander and lies abroad. Therefore the leaders of the German liberation movement have decided to defend themselves against this criminal slander, and from Saturday, April 1, 1933, at 10 a.m., to oberserve against all Jewish shops, warehouses, lawyers' practices etc.

A BOYCOTT

We appeal to you, German men and women, to observe this boycott. Don't buy in Jewish shops or warehouses! Don't engage Jewish lawyers, avoid Jewish doctors! Show the Jews that they cannot disgrace and defile Germany's honour without being punished. Those who ignore this appeal prove that they sympathize with Germany's enemies.

Long live the honourable General Field-Marshall of the Great War, the President of the Reich PAUL VON HINDENBURG!
Long live the Führer and Chancellor ADOLF HITLER!
Long live the German people and the holy GERMAN FATHERLAND!

58
In May 1933, books by
"undesirable authors" are
publicly burnt.

Their books were burnt:

Schalom Asch	Karl Kautsky	Theodor Plivier
Bert Brecht	Alfred Kerr	Erich Maria Remarque
Max Brod	Hermann Kesten	Ludwig Renn
Lion Feuchtwanger	Egon Erwin Kisch	Arthur Schnitzler
Alfred Döblin	Emil Ludwig	Adrienne Thomas
Leonhard Frank	Heinrich Mann	Ernst Toller
Sigmund Freud	Klaus Mann	Kurt Tucholsky
Ernst Glaeser	Karl Marx	Jakob Wassermann
Walter Hasenclever	Alfred Neumann	Theodor Wolff
Theodor Heuss	Robert Neumann	Arnold Zweig
Erich Kästner	Carl von Ossietzky	Stefan Zweig

and those of many other authors.

"This was but a prelude;
where books are burnt
human-beings will be burnt
in the end"
The German poet Heinrich Heine in 1820

Some of the first measures taken after the seizure of power

S. A. men are trained as "Police auxiliaries"

61

63

THE NEW BAVARIA
The first Measures of the Provisional Bavarian Government—Drastic Intervention against Reds who are undermining the State—Lord Mayor Scharnagel dismissed—Peaceful Take Over of Political Power—

PROCLAMATION OF THE "REICHSKOMMISSAR"
In accordance with § 2 of the order for the protection of the people and State, the Minister of the Interior has in the name of the government of the Reich extended federal jurisdiction to include Bavaria. I have been entrusted with the execution of these measures and have already taken charge of the entire police force.
The following have been appointed commissioners with special duties:
Captain a. D. Ernst Röhm
The MP and town councillor Hermann Esser
I have also appointed as my deputies:
for the Ministry of the Interior: Adolf Wagner MP
for the Ministry of Justice: Dr. Frank MP
for the Treasury: Lord Mayor Siebert MP
I have appointed the Reichstag MP Himmler as Police President for Munich.
The appointments by the Commissioner of the Reich are intended to preserve public order and security until a constitutional government is formed in Bavaria, in keeping with the wishes expressed by the overwhelming majority of the Bavarian "patriotic" population and guaranteeing loyal Bavarian supporters for the government of Adolf Hitler's national uprising.
I expect all Bavarians who love their nation and homeland to support me in my struggle against the undermining of the nation by the Marxist and their sympathizers.
Long live our German Fatherland!
Long live the Bavarian Homeland!
                    The Representative of the
                    Government of the Reich
                    Franz von Epp

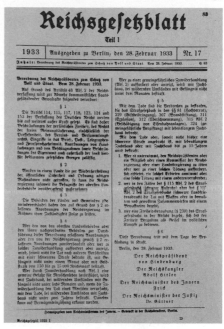

LEGAL BULLETIN OF THE REICH No 17

Part I

Published in Berlin

Presidential order for the protection of the state and people.
February 28, 1933

In accordance with article 48 § 2 of the Constitution of the Reich the following has been ordered as protection against Communist subversive activities which represent a danger to the state.

1

Articlels 114, 115, 117, 118, 123, 124, and 153 of the Constitution are invalid until further notice. Restrictions on the freedom of the individual, the right to free speech, including freedom of the press and the right of assembly and to form groups, infringements on the secrecy of post, telegraph and telephone communications, house searches, confiscation and limitation in property ownership over and above the previously legally specified limitations, are now permissible.

2

The government of the Reich is authorized to take over provisional control of states which do not implement the measures necessary to ensure the reestablishment of public order and security.

3

In accordance with § 2 all state and municipal authorities are to respect the sovereignty of the government of the Reich.

4

State authorities or subsidiaries under their jurisdiction who obstruct the execution of these orders, or § 2 of the government order, or those who encourage or incite such opposition will receive a prison sentence of not less than one month or a fine of 150 to 150000 Reichsmarks, unless they have allready been sentenced to a more severe punishment under existing regulations. Those who endanger human life by their opposition will be sentenced to penal servitude, or in extenuating circumstances to a term of imprisonment of not less than 6 months, and those who cause loss of life will be sentenced to death or in extenuating circumstances to a term of penal servitude of not less than 2 years.

In addition, confiscation of personal property can be ordered. Those who encourage or incite opposition (§ 2) and thereby endanger the public will be sentenced to penal servitude, or in extenuating circumstances, to a term of imprisonment of not less than three months.

5

Crimes which in the existing penal code are punishavle by life imprisonment i. e. §§ 81 (high treason), 229 (poisoning), 307 (arson), 311 (causing an explosion), 312 (flooding), 315 part 2 (damaging of railway installations), 324 (large scale poisoning), shall now be punishable by death.

The following crimes are to be punished by death or with life long penal scrvitude or penal servitude of up to 15 years:

1. Those who attempt to assassinate the President of the Reich, or a member or deputy to assassinate the President of the Reich, or a state. Those who encourage, aid and abet or conspire with other persons to cary out such an assassination.

2. Those who according to § 5 part 2 (incitement to riot) or § 125 part 2 (severe breach of the public peace) of the penal code, make use of fire arms or deliberately and knowingly negotiate with armed persons.

3. Those who according to § 239 of the penal code rob a person of his freeedom with the intent to use him as a political hostage in their political struggle.

This decree takes effect from the date of its proclamation.

Berlin, February 28, 1933
The President von Hindenburg
The Chancellor Adolf Hitler
The Minister of the Interior Frick
The Minister of Justice Dr. Gürtner

Weitere Verhaftungen in München

Während des Verdacht des Separatismus zu der Verhaftung der beiden Schriftleiter der „Münchener Neuesten Nachrichten", von Aretin und Büchner, führte, wurde heute morgen unter dem Verdacht bolschewistischer Umtriebe der Hauptschriftleiter, der dem gleichen Verlag angehörenden „Münchener Illustrierten Presse", Lorant, ebenfalls verhaftet.

Der Verhaftete ist ungarischer Jude und besitzt nicht die deutsche Staatsbürgerschaft.

Der Direktor Falkenberg des Münchener Schauspielhauses ist unter dem Verdacht, bolschewistischer Verbindungsmann zu sein, in Haft genommen worden. Seine Mitdirektoren, die Juden Geller und Fischer, sind nach Karlsbad und Prag entflohen.

64

FURTHER ARRESTS IN MUNICH

Whereas the two leading journalists von Aretin and Büchner have been arrested as alleged separatists, the chief editor of the Munich Illustrated Press, Lorant, employed by the same publishers, has been arrested today because of alleged Bolshevist activities. Lorant is a Hungarian Jew without German citizenship. Director Falkkenberg of the Munich Theatre has been arrested as an alleged Bolshevist agent. His co-directors Geller and Fischer have fled to Karlsbad and Prague.

Schutzhaft für kommunistische und Reichsbanner-Funktionäre

Der Reichskommissar erließ einen Funkspruch an die Polizei folgenden Inhalts:

Funkspruch an die Polizeidirektionen und Staatspolizeiämter.

Ersuche sofort sämtliche kommunistischen Funktionäre und Reichsbannerführer im Interesse der öffentlichen Sicherheit in Schutzhaft zu nehmen und Waffensuchungen vorzunehmen. Sofortige Anzeige an das Innenministerium. Der Aufziehung der Hakenkreuzfahne an öffentlichen Gebäuden keinen Widerstand entgegensetzen. Alle Polizeidoppelposten sind mit je einem SA- oder SS. zu stellen; dieser ist von der Polizei mit Pistole zu bewaffnen. Gegen alle Gesetzwidrigkeiten und gegen Widerstände gegen die Anordnungen der Beauftragten der Reichsregierung mit aller Strenge vorgehen. Erwarte pünktlichen Vollzug. Regierungen und Bezirksämter verständigen.

66

Protective Custody for Communist and "Reichsbanner"-Functionaries.

The Reichs Commissioner cabled the following to the police: Cable to the Police Headquarters and the State Police Offices. In the interests of public security, request all Communist functionaries and "Reichsbanner" leaders taken into protective custody and a search for weapons be conducted. Immediate report to the Ministry of the Interior. The hoisting of the swastika flag on public buildings is not to be hindered. All police patrols are to include an SA or SS man who is to be armed with a pistol by the police. Proceed with utmost severity against all unlawfulness and opposition to the orders of the Reich government's representatives. Expect punctual execution. Government and district offices to be notified.

Aufsehenerregende Verhaftungen in München

München, 13. März

Am Montag wurden der Chefredakteur der „Münchener Neuesten Nachrichten", Fritz Büchner, und der politische Schriftleiter dieses Blattes, Freiherr von Aretin, in Schutzhaft genommen, weil Verdacht besteht, daß die beiden mit Männern in Verbindung stehen, die die Loslösung Bayerns vom Reich betreiben.

Bei Durchsuchung der Wohnung des Freiherrn von Aretin wurde dort der Nichtreichsdeutsche von Strachwitz, ein Mitarbeiter des „Geraden Weg", angetroffen, der sich ohne polizeiliche Erlaubnis in München aufhielt.

Im Laufe des Sonntags war Graf Anton Arco in Schutzhaft genommen worden, nachdem der Polizei bekannt geworden war, daß er in Freundeskreisen Äußerungen getan habe, es käme ihm nicht darauf an, wie einst Eisner, so auch Adolf Hitler zu beseitigen. Auf der Polizeidirektion richtete der zuständige Beamte die ehrenwörtliche Frage an Graf Arco, ob er Drohungen gebraucht habe. Dieser verweigerte darauf die Antwort.

1. Allen Beamten und Lehrern, die der kommunistischen Partei angehören, wird mit sofortiger Wirkung die Ausübung ihres Dienstes untersagt. Gegen die Beamten und Lehrer ist mit größter Beschleunigung das förmliche Dienststrafverfahren auf Dienstentlassung einzuleiten.

2. Diese Verordnung gilt für die Beamten und Lehrer des Staates der Gemeinden, der Bezirks- und Zweckverbände und der sonstigen einer Landesaufsicht unterstehenden Körperschaften des öffentlichen Rechtes, bei denen öffentlich-rechtliche Beamte angestellt sind.

65

SPECTACULAR ARRESTS IN MUNICH

Munich March 13

Fritz Büchner, the chief editor, and Freiherr von Aretin, the political editor of the "Münchner Neueste Nachrichten", have been taken into protective custody because of suspected contact with persons who are attempting to separate Bavaria from the rest of the Reich. The non-Reich German von Strachwitz, a co-editor of the "Gerader Weg", was discovered in Freiherr von Aretin's apartment during a house search. He had been staying in Munich without being officially registered. On Saturday, Count Anton Arco was taken into protective custody after it had come to police notice that he had remarked in the company of friends that he could eliminate Adolf Hitler just as he had once eliminated Eisner. At the police station the police officer responsible asked Count Arco, on his word of honour, whether or not he had made such threats. He refused to answer.

70

67

68

POLICE INSTRUCTIONS

Measures against immorality and hostility towards the State

In accordance with § 14 of the police administration law which states that the police force is obliged to protect the State from dangers to public law and order, the "Deutsche Polizei Beamter", the official organ of the "Kameradschaftsbund", outlines rules and regulations which are also of importance when dealing with the general public. For example those who, on festive occasions, deliberately decline from observing the Hitler salute whilst singing the Horst Wessel song, manifest hostility towards the State. If the refusal to observe the usual German greeting towards civil servants or the administrative authority, is deliberate and manifests disrespect, it must be regarded as a danger to public security. GROUSERS AND GRUMBLERS oppose the National Socialist State and present a danger to public security. Landlords refusing to take in large Arian families are acting against the interests of the national community and are undermining the preservation of the race. Persons who commit suicide harm state interests (i. e. potential labour force, military service). False unfounded rumours regarding state affairs endanger state stability and public security. He who harms the movement also harms Germany. All actions and declarations of any kind which are detrimental to Adolf Hitler's state, his efforts and aims JUSTIFY POLICE INTERVENTION.

All symptoms of moral decline and confusion which have been manifest until now must be prevented. Any German girl who is seen with a Jew in public offends racial sensitivity and thereby public order. Indecent dancing offends our racial honour and is forbidden by the police. If Arians attempt to sell to Jews German land which is considered to be a substantial part of the German National wealth, the police may intervene. The application of measures, dutifully judged to be necessary, must comply with the ideals and standards of the National Socialist Party ethic, for example preferential treatment of expectant mothers or mothers with many children in respect to traffic regulations etc. as well as preferential treatment of veterans. These regulations for the German police are for the most part based on precedential court findings.

Baiting of arrested Social Democrats and Jewish citizens

71

The "Stürmer"
Ritual Murder Issue

JEWISH MURDER PROGRAMME
AGAINST NON-JEWISH HUMAN-
ITY UNVEILED

For thousands of years the Yid has spilled
Man's blood, his sacred rites to build;
Upon our necks the fiend still sits,
It's up to you to see he flits.

THE JEWS ARE OUR DOWNFALL!

72

THE RITUAL MURDER ISSUE OF THE "STÜR-
MER" CONFISCATED

By order of the Chancellor the special issue of the
"Stürmer" entitled "Ritual Murder" has been con-
fiscated as it contains an attack on Christ's Holy
Communion.

NUREMBERG CLERGY PROTEST
AGAINST THE RITUAL MURDER ISSUE OF THE
"STÜRMER"

In connection with the Chancellor's confiscation
order of the Ritual Murder issue of the "Stürmer"
the Protestant Church of Nuremberg has, in its
entirety, issued the following statement:
In the special issue of the weekly newspaper the
"Stürmer" of May 1, 1934, reference is made to
the Holy Communion in connection with the Jewish ritual murders. We publicly protest before
God and our entire congregation against this atro-
cious attack on the Church's Holy Sacrament. It is
a blasphemy not only against Christ but against
God himself.

73

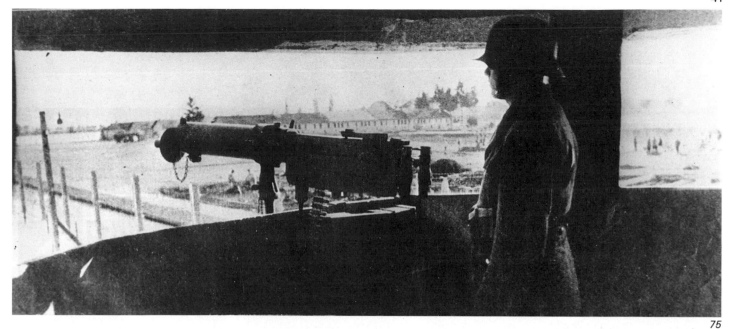

75

Plan of the Dachau Concentration Camp

74

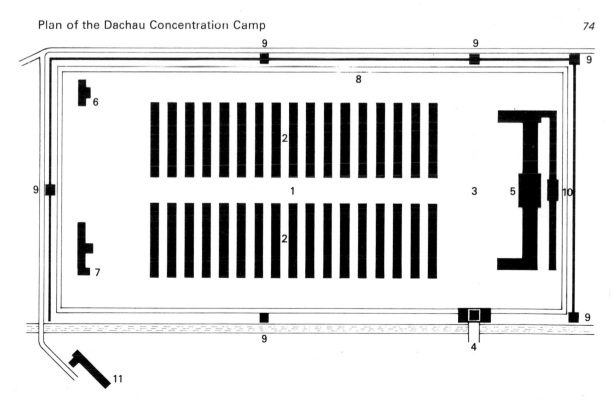

1. "Lagerstrasse", Main Road
2. Barracks
3. Parade Ground for Roll Call
4. "Jourhaus", Entrance to the Camp and Guard Room
5. "Wirtschaftsgebäude", Kitchen, Laundry, Showers etc.
6. Disinfection Hut

7. Vegetable Garden
8. Ditch with live barbed-wire Fence and Camp Wall
9. Watch Towers
10. "Bunker", Prison Block
11. Crematorium

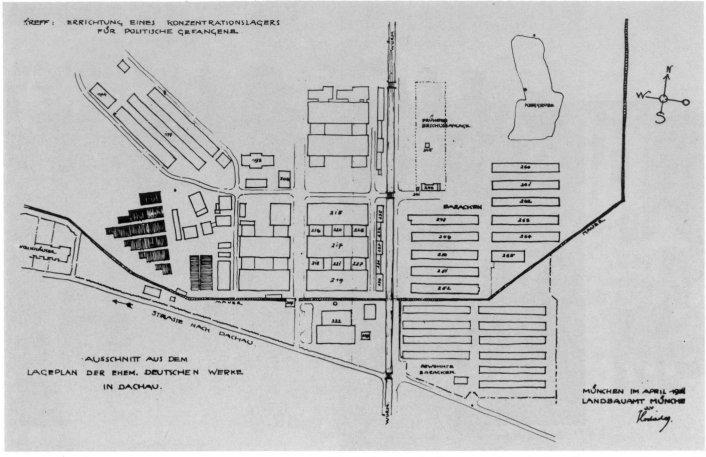

TREFF: ERRICHTUNG EINES KONZENTRATIONSLAGERS
FÜR POLITISCHE GEFANGENE.

AUSSCHNITT AUS DEM
LAGEPLAN DER EHEM. DEUTSCHEN WERKE
IN DACHAU.

MÜNCHEN IM APRIL 1933
LANDBAUAMT MÜNCHEN

The first concentration camp, installed in a former mun‌ *80*
factory

81

Concentration Camp Dachau
Commandant's Office
No. K 125/37   Dachau, January 18, 1937

Sub: Building project in Dachau Concentration Camp

Re: none

Encl: none

To:

''Landbauamt'' (district board of public works)
Oberbaurat Neidhart
München

Subsequent to talks held with Oberbaurat Neidhart, headquarters of Dachau
concentration camp requests that the approved 22 000 RM be transferred to
the camp administration, since work on the construction site has already
been started on mutual agreement.

The Camp Commandant

82
Völkischer
Beobachter,
March 21, 1933

Tuesday, March 21, 1933
Concentration Camp for Protective Custody Prisoners in Bavaria.
Munich, March 20,
Police headquarters have received numerous enquiries regarding the duration of protective custody. The Chief of Police, Himmler, stated that it is necessary to classify the unexpectedly large amount of material which we were able to confiscate, and that all enquiries only hinder this work. Each enquiry means another day's custody for the prisoner in question.

Chief of Police Himmler took this opportunity to repudiate all rumours of ill-treatment of the prisoners.
It has become necessary to make some changes in the prisoners' accommodation.
On Wednesday, the first concentration camp will be opened near Dachau to accommodate 5000 prisoners.
Here, all Communist, and where necessary "Reichsbanner" and Social Democrat functionaries who endanger state security, will be interned together as their continued stay in normal state prisons is proving too great a burden. Experience has shown that these people cannot be granted their freedom as they continue to agitate and create unrest when released. In order to ensure state security, we must adopt these measures regardless of any petty considerations. The Police and Ministry of the Interior are convinced that they are thus acting in the national interest and that these measures will have a calming effect upon the whole nation.
Continued Prohibition of Social Democrat Newspaper
Munich, March 20,
State Commissioner Esser announced on march 20, 1933, that in accordance with regulations governing all other districts of the Reich, and in order to avoid all possibilities which could endanger public peace and order, the ban on all Social Democratic periodicals will be continued for the period from March 21 to April 4, 1933

Münchner Neueste Nachrichten

Ein Konzentrationslager für politische Gefangene

In der Nähe von Dachau

In einer Pressebesprechung teilte der kommissarische Polizeipräsident von München Himmler mit:

Am Mittwoch wird in der Nähe von Dachau das erste Konzentrationslager eröffnet. Es hat ein Fassungsvermögen von 5000 Menschen. Hier werden die gesamten kommunistischen und — soweit notwendig — Reichsbanner- und marxistischen Funktionäre, die die Sicherheit des Staates gefährden, zusammengezogen, da es auf die Dauer nicht möglich ist, wenn der Staatsapparat nicht so sehr belästet werden soll, die einzelnen kommunistischen Funktionäre in den Gerichtsgefängnissen zu lassen, während es andererseits auch nicht angängig ist, diese Funktionäre wieder in die Freiheit zu lassen. Bei einzelnen Versuchen, die wir gemacht haben, war der Erfolg der, daß sie weiter hetzen und zu organisieren versuchen. Wir haben diese Maßnahme ohne jede Rücksicht auf kleinliche Bedenken getroffen in der Ueberzeugung, damit zur Beruhigung der nationalen Bevölkerung und in ihrem Sinn zu handeln.

Weiter versicherte Polizeipräsident Himmler, daß die Schutzhaft in den einzelnen Fällen nicht länger aufrechterhalten werde, als notwendig sei. Es sei aber selbstverständlich, daß das Material, das in ungeahnter Menge beschlagnahmt wurde, zur Sichtung längere Zeit benötigt. Die Polizei werde dabei nur aufgehalten, wenn dauernd angefragt werde, wann dieser oder jener Schutzhäftling freigelassen werde. Wie unrichtig die vielfach verbreiteten Gerüchte über die Behandlung von Schutzhäftlingen seien, gehe daraus hervor, daß einigen Schutzhäftlingen, die es wünschten, wie z. B. Dr. Gerlich und Frhr. v. Aretin, priesterlicher Zuspruch anstandslos genehmigt worden sei.

---

83 Münchner Neueste Nachrichten
Tuesday, March 21, 1933

A CONCENTRATION CAMP FOR POLITICAL PRISONERS NEAR DACHAU

The Munich Chief of Police, Himmler, has issued the following press announcement:

On Wednesday the first concentration camp is to be opened near Dachau with accommodation for 5000 persons. All Communist and-where necessary- "Reichsbanner" and Social Democrat functionaries who endanger state security are to be concentrated here, as in the long term it is not possible to keep individual functionaries in the state prisons without overburdening these prisons, and on the other hand these people cannot be released because attempts have shown that they persist in their efforts to aitate and organize as soon as they are released. We have taken these measures without regard to any petty considerations and are convinced they will have a calming effect upon the nation in whose interest we have acted.

Police Chief Himmler further assured that protective custody is only to be enforced as long as necessary. It is of course obvious that the classification of the unexpectedly large amounts of confiscated material will take a long time and that continual inquiries as to the date of release of individual protective custody prisoners will only hinder the police in their work. The widespread rumours regarding the treatment of prisoners are shown to be inaccurate by the fact that requests by some protective custody prisoners to talk to a priest were granted without hesitation, as for example in the cases of Dr. Gerlich and Frhr. v. Aretin.

Warnung!

Am 30. Mai wurden an der Umgebungsmauer des Konzentrationslagers in Dachau zwei Personen beobachtet, die versuchten, über die Mauer hinwegzuschauen. Selbstverständlich wurden sie sofort festgenommen. Sie erklärten, aus Neugierde, wie das Lager von innen aussehe, über die Mauer geschaut zu haben. Um ihren Wissensdurst befriedigen zu können, und ihnen hierzu Gelegenheit zu geben, wurden sie eine Nacht im Konzentrationslager behalten.

Hoffentlich ist ihre Neugierde nunmehr befriedigt, wenn dies auch auf etwas unvorhergesehene Weise geschehen ist.

Sollten weitere Neugierige sich nicht abhalten lassen, dem Verbot zuwiderhandelnd über die Mauer zu schauen, so sei ihnen jetzt schon zur Befriedigung ihrer Neugierde mitgeteilt, daß die Folgenden nicht nur eine Nacht, sondern länger Gelegenheit zum Studium des Lagers bekommen werden.

Neugierige sind hiemit nochmals gewarnt.

Der Beauftragte der obersten SA-Führung:
Sonderkommissar Friedrichs.

---

87 Warning!

On May 30, two persons were observed trying to look over the wall surrounding the concentration camp in Dachau. They were of course immediately arrested. They explained that they had been curious to see what the camp looked like inside. In order to give them the opportunity to satisfy their curiosity they were detained overnight. It is hoped that their curiosity has now been satisfied in spite of this unforeseen measure.

We wish to still the curiosity of all those who might ignore this warning by informing them that in the future they will be given the opportunity of studying the camp from inside for longer than just one night.

All inquisitive persons are hereby warned once more.

In charge of the Supreme S.A. Command
Special Commissioner Friedrichs
Amper Bote No 129, June 2, 1933

The population of the concentration camps is increasing.

As already reported the concentration camp erected on the site of the former munitions factory was opened yesterday. To begin with about sixty left wing persons are being held there under the supervision of County Police, SS and SA members.

Münchner Neueste Nachrichten, March 23, 1933

Das Konzentrationslager bevölkert sich. Gestern wurde, wie angekündigt, das Konzentrationslager auf dem Gelände der ehemaligen Pulverfabrik in Dachau in Betrieb genommen. Zunächst wurden etwa 60 linksgerichtete Personen im Lager untergebracht. Die Bewachung wird durch Landespolizei und durch S.S.= und S.A.=Männer durchgeführt.

Protective Custody Prisoners cutting Turf.

For some weeks now one has been able to observe prisoners working in the marshes near Eschenhof. As we have learned the administration of the Dachau concentration camp has bought an area of turf land in Gröbenzell from the farmer Dinkler (party member) where the prisoners are employed in cutting turf. Because of the large quantities involved, work on the turf-cutting is expected to last some considerable time. The prisoners, guarded by S.S. and S.A. men, are staying in the farm buildings. They are said to spend their free time quite contentedly in the pursuit of games and sport etc. During the day they can be seen quite happily at work. Of course, the prisoners working in the marshes as well as those working in the camp, are not allowed to approach or converse with strangers. Members of the public are requested not to loiter in the area.

Amper Bote No. 211, Sept. 7, 1933

Schutzhaftgefangene beim Torfstechen. Schon seit einigen Wochen kann man im Moos beim Eschenhof Gefangene arbeiten sehen. Wie wir nun dazu erfahren, hat die Verwaltung des Dachauer Konzentrationslagers vom Pg. Gutsbesitzer Dinkler, Gröbenzell Torf (bzw. Torfstich) gekauft, den die Lagerinsassen nun selbst stechen. Für diese Arbeit sind ca. 160 Mann ausersehen worden und zwar sollen es meist Leute aus dem Donaumoos sein, die mit dem Torfstechen und -behandeln bereits vertraut waren. Da größere Quantitäten in Frage kommen dürften, ist noch mit längerer Dauer dieser Torfarbeiten zu rechnen. Die unter S.S.- und S.A.-Bewachung stehende Inhaftierten-Gruppe ist im Dinklerschen Gutshofe selbst einquartiert und soll sich in der Freizeit mit Spiel, Sport usw. aufs beste unterhalten. Tagsüber kann man die Schutzhäftlinge frohgemut arbeiten sehen. Annäherungen oder Gespräche mit fremden Personen sind den Torfarbeitern selbstverständlich ebenso untersagt wie den beim Lager selbst Arbeitenden. Auch hier wird die Bevölkerung ersucht, nicht unnötig herumzustehen.

Unsuccessful Escape Attempt from the Dachau Concentration Camp

Munich: According to the Munich Police Report four communist detainees attempted to escape from the Dachau concentration camp on Wednesday afternoon. As the prisoners ignored an order to halt, the guards opened fire, killing three of the communistes and seriously injuring the other.

Amper Bote No 89/90, April 14, 1933

Mißglückter Fluchtversuch im Konzentrationslager Dachau

München. Der Münchner Polizeibericht teilt mit: Am Mittwoch nachmittag unternahmen vier von den im Konzentrationslager Dachau untergebrachten Kommunisten einen Fluchtversuch. Da sie auf die Haltrufe der Posten nicht hörten, gaben die Posten Schüsse ab, wobei drei Kommunisten getötet und einer schwer verletzt wurden.

München. Wie der „Völkische Beobachter" meldet, wurde in Wegarn bei Miesbach die 1. Hitlerjugend-Führer-Schule im Gebiet Hochland eröffnet.

Mailand. Die italienischen Blätter veröffentlichen einen Artikel Mussolinis. Ausgehend von der Tatsache, daß die kleine Entente plötzlich als 5. Großmacht Europas auf der Bildfläche auftaucht, legt Mussolini dar, daß sämtliche Voraussetzungen für eine solche Großmacht fehlen. Weiter sagt Mussolini, es würden schwere Komplikationen vermieden werden, wenn man die Friedensverträge, die revidiert werden müssen, revidiere. Eine Revision, die einen

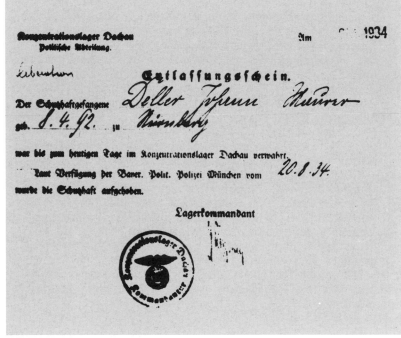

89

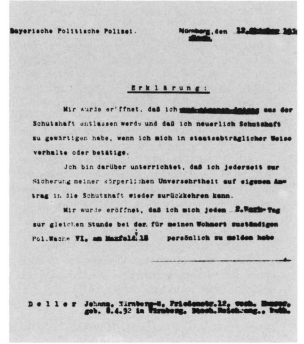

90

Bayerische Politische Polizei   Nürnberg
Oct 12, 1934

Concentration Camp Dachau
Political Department   Date . . .

Certificate of Discharge

The Protective Custody Prisoner Deller Johann, bricklayer, born: April 8, 1892 in Nuremberg has been held in custody in Dachau concentration camp until today. In accordance with the order of the Bavarian Political Police, Munich, of Aug 20, 1934 protective custody has been suspended.

            The Commandant

STATEMENT

I have been informed of my release from protective custody and that any further activity or behaviour detrimental to the State on my part will lead to renewed protective custody.
I am aware that I may at any time apply for a further period of protective custody if I consider my physical well-being to be in jeopardy. I have been informed that I must report in person to Police Station VI—Marsfeld 18, every second working day at the same time.

        Deller Johann
        Nürnberg-N, Friedensstr. 12
        born April 8, 1892, in Nürnberg

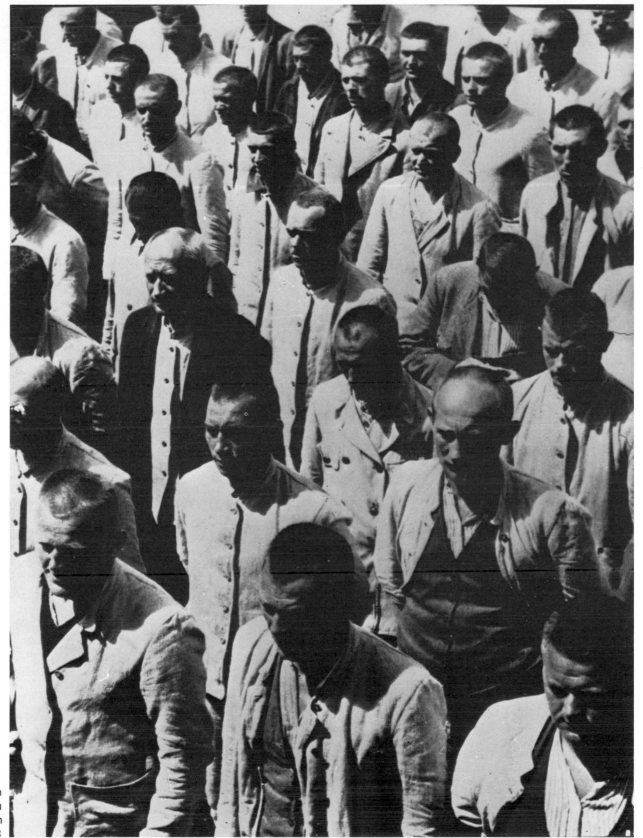

88
Roll-call in
the Dachau
concentration
camp in 1933

Vorb. Häftl. — Schutzh. — Schulungsh. — Rückf. Häftl. — Bibelf. — § 175
(Zutreffendes unterstreichen!)

Häftl. Nr. _____ Block: _____

Name: _____ Vornamen: _____

Beruf: _____ geb. am: _____

zu: _____ Relig. _____ Stand: _____

Staatsangeh.: _____

(Anschrift der Angehörigen: Name, Vorname, Ort, Straße, Hausnummer.)

(Eingeliefert von welcher örtl. Dienststelle.)

(Wohnort nach der Entlassung, Straße, Hausnummer.)

In Strafhaft vom: _____ bis: _____ in: _____

In Haft, bezw. Schutzhaft seit: _____ Im Konz. Lager seit: _____

Die Invalidenkarte, bezw. Angestelltenversicherungskarte befindet sich:

Mitglied einer Sonderkasse:

Überstellt am: _____ nach: _____

Entlassen am: _____ nach: _____

Bemerkungen: _____

Concentration camp questionnaire   91

Prisoner's number and classification   92

Form listing the personal effects of the prisoners ranging from articles of
clothing and cuff-links to cigarette papers.   95   96

Vor- und Zuname: _____ Haft-Nr. _____

Beruf: _____ geboren am: _____ in: _____

Anschrifts-Ort: _____ Straße Nr. _____

Eingel. am: ____ / ____ Uhr von _____ Entl. am ____ / ____ Uhr nach _____

Bei Einlieferung abgegeben: Koffer   Aktentasche   Paket

Hut/Mütze	Paar Schuhe/Stiefel	Kragenknöpfe	Feuerzeug	Wehrpaß
Mantel	Paar Strümpfe	Halstuch	Tabak	Pfeife	Fremdenpaß
Rock	Jacke	Paar Gamaschen Tuch Leder	Taschentuch	Zigarren/Zigaretten	Arbeitsbuch
Weste/Kletterweste	Kragen	Paar Handschuhe Tuch Leder	Sig.-Blättchen	Invalidenkarte
Hose	Vorhemd	Brieftasche mit	Ziertuch	
Pullover	Binder/Fliege	Papiere	Messer	Schere
Oberhemden	Paar Armelhalter	Sporthemd/Hosen	Bleistift/Drehblei	
Unterhemden	Paar Sockenhalter	Abzeichen	Geldbörse	
Unterhosen	Paar Mansch.-Knöpfe	Schlüssel a. Ring	Kamm	Wertsachen: ja—nein

Abgabe bestätigt: Effektenverwalter:

_____   _____

KL/3/9 44 100.000

Häftl.-Nr.

Name: _____

geb. _____

Inhalt:

Taschenuhr, gelb/weiss mit Kette gelb/weiss

Armbanduhr, gelb/weiss mit Metallband/Lederband

Ehering gelb / weiss

Siegel-Ring, gelb / weiss mit / ohne Stein

Manschettenknöpfe, gelb / weiss

KL/37/4.43 500.000

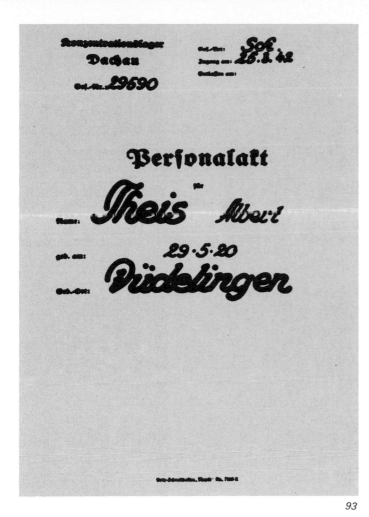

93

94

CONCENTRATION CAMP DACHAU
Prisoner No. 29 590

Type of custody: p. c.
Date of admittance: March 23, 1942
Date of discharge:

Personal Records

Name: Theis, Albert
Born: May 29, 1920
Place of birth: Düdelingen

Concentration Camp Dachau—Type of Custody: Protective Custody—Ref. No. 29 590

Surname, First name:	Theis Albert		
Date of birth:	May 29, 1920	in:	Düdelingen
District:	Esch/Alzig	Country:	Luxembourg
Domicile:	Düdelingen	Street:	Keiler 40
District:	see above		
Marital Status:	single	Occupation:	clerk
Nationality:	Luxembourg	Religion:	Roman Catholic
Father:	Nikolaus	Occupation:	clerk
Mother:	Anna	née:	Feltgen
		Race:	Aryan
Domicile of parents:	Düdelingen	Street:	see above
Wife:	none	née:	
		Race:	
Next of kin:	parents: Nikolaus and Anna Theis		
Domicile:	Düdelingen	Street:	Keiler 40
District:	Esch/Alzig	Country:	Luxembourg
Children:	none		

Arrested on:	March 23, 1942 in: Innsbruck	
Admitted on:		
Admitted by:	Stapo Innsbruck	
Reason for admittance:		
Party membership:	from:	to:
Function:		
Membership of affiliated organizations:		
Previous criminal convictions:		
Previous political convictions:		
In protective custody in:	from:	to:

I have been instructed that I will be punished for document forgery if the above statement should prove to be false.

The Commandant

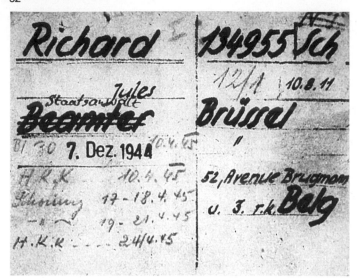

Richard   134955 Sch

Jules   12/1   10.8.11

Staatsanwalt

Beamter   Brüssel

7. Dez. 1944   10.4.45

H.R.K.   10.4.45   52, Avenue Brugmann

17 - 18.4.45

19 - 21.4.45   u. 3. r.k. Belg

H.K.K.   24/4.45

97

Brichaux   40542 Sch

Jean   8/3   21.10.26

Photograf

L.arbeiter   1/Bons

12.7. 25.11.42   - 11 -

DRW   Fonequois 196

Zed. r.k. Belg

Vater: Nikolas B.

w.o.

98

Mauroy   110.662 Sch

Charles   26/1   12.6.93

r.k. Geistl.   Temploux

21. Sep. 1944   Namur

H.A.   35, rue de Fer

l. - r.k. Belg

Bek: Marcel Dourier

Forcheim/Bayer.

National Hotel

99

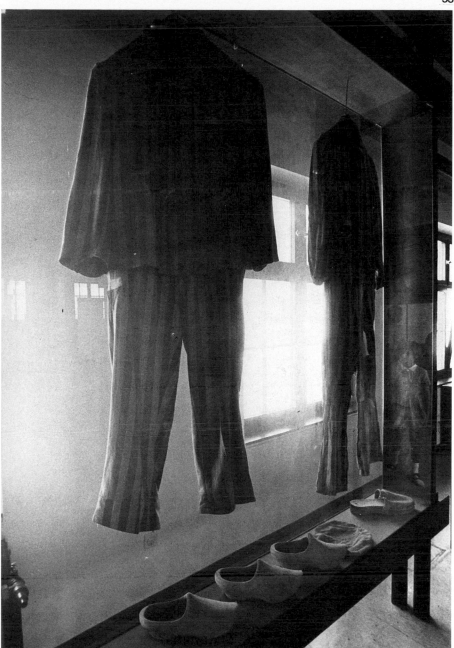

100

Geheime Staatspolizei

Geheimes Staatspolizeiamt

Berlin SW 11, den ....5..... 194.
Prinz-Albrecht-Straße 8

.S.A. IV C H H.Nr. ...23051

Schutzhaftbefehl

Vor- und Zuname: Adolf Maislinger

Geburtstag und -Ort: 9.12.03 München

Beruf: Schlosser

Familienstand: led.

Staatsangehörigkeit: DR.

Religion: kath.

Raffe (bei Nichtariern anzugeben):

Wohnort und Wohnung: zul. München, Oberländerstr. 15

wird in Schutzhaft genommen.

Gründe:

Er — Sie — gefährdet nach dem Ergebnis der staatspolizeilichen Feststellungen durch sein — ihr — Verhalten den Bestand und die Sicherheit des Volkes und Staates, indem er — sie — nach Verbüssung einer längeren Zuchthausstrafe wegen Vorbereitung zum Hochverrat zu der Befürchtung Veranlassung gibt, er werde sich in Freiheit weiterhin für den Kommunismus betätigen.

Für die Richtigkeit:

Secret State Police
Secret State Police Office
S.A. IV C H H.Nr. – 23051

Berlin SW 11, September 8, 1942
Prinz Albrechtstr. 8

PROTECTIVE CUSTODY ORDER

Christian name and surname:	Adolf Maislinger
Date and place of birth:	Dec 9, 1903, Munich
Occupation:	locksmith
Status:	single
Nationality:	German
Religion:	Roman Catholic
Race (in case of non-Arians):	
Domicile:	(last:) Munich, Oberländerstr. 15

is to be taken into protective custody.

Reasons:
State Police evidence shows that his/her behaviour constitutes a danger to the existence and security of state and people:
After having served a long term of penal servitude for planned high treason, it is feared that he would continue his communist activities upon release.

signed:

Geheime Staatspolizei

Geheimes Staatspolizeiamt

Berlin SW 11, den 13. April 1942.
Prinz Albrecht-Straße 8

IV G 2 H. Nr. F.8833.

Schutzhaftbefehl

Vor- und Zuname: Johannes Flintrop

Geburtstag und -Ort: 23.5.1904 in Wuppertal-Barmen

Beruf: Kaplan

Familienstand: led.

Staatsangehörigkeit: RD.

Religion: kath.

Raffe (bei Nichtariern anzugeben):

Wohnort und Wohnung: Lettmann, Schlageterstr. 21

wird in Schutzhaft genommen.

Gründe:

Er — sie — gefährdet nach dem Ergebnis der staatspolizeilichen Feststellungen durch sein — ihr — Verhalten den Bestand und die Sicherheit des Volkes und Staates, indem er — sie — ungeachtet einer früheren, wegen seiner staatsabträglichen Haltung erfolgten staatspolizeilichen Beanstandung sein geistliches Amt dazu missbraucht, durch defaitistische Äußerungen Unruhe und Erregung hervorzurufen, die geeignet sind, den Glauben des deutschen Volkes an den Endsieg und die unveränderte Schlagkraft der Wehrmacht zu erschüttern.

gez. Müller.

Beglaubigt:

D 42 Schutzhaftbefehl des Kaplans Flintrop, 1942

Secret State Police
Secret State Police Office
IV G 2 W Nr. F 8833

Berlin SW 11, April 13, 1942
Prinz Albrechtstr. 8

PROTECTIVE CUSTODY ORDER

Christian name and surname:	Johannes Flintrop
Date and place of birth:	May 23, 1904 – Wuppertal-Barmen
Occupation:	Chaplain
Status:	single
Nationality:	German
Religion:	Roman Catholic
Race (in case of non-Arians):	
Domicile:	Lettmann, Schlageterstr. 21

is to be taken into protective custody

Reasons:
State Police evidence shows that his/her behaviour constitutes a danger to the existence and security of people and state because:
Ignoring an earlier police complaint regarding his detrimental attitude towards the State he has abused his clerical position to make defeatist remarks to create unrest and commotion which could serve to shake the German People's faith in the ultimate victory and unfailing strength of our armed forces.

signed:

Geheime Staatspolizei

Geheimes Staatspolizeiamt

B.-Nr.   -II B Haftn.B.8298-

Berlin SW 11, den   6.Februar   193 9.
Prinz-Albrecht-Straße 8

Schutzhaftbefehl

Vor- und Zuname: Gottlieb B r a n z,

Geburtstag und -Ort: 13.9.1896 München,

Beruf: Vertreter,

Familienstand: verh.,

Staatsangehörigkeit: DR.,

Religion: freireligiös

Raffe (bei Nichtariern anzugeben):   arisch

Wohnort und Wohnung: München, Aignerstr.32/o.

wird in Schutzhaft genommen.

Gründe:

Er — Sie — gefährdet nach dem Ergebnis der staatspolizeilichen Feststellungen durch sein — ihr — Verhalten den Bestand und die Sicherheit des Volkes und Staates, indem er — Sie — auf Grund seines Vorlebens zu befürchten steht, er würde sich, in Freiheit belassen, weiter in illegal für den Marxismus betätigen..

gez. Heydrich.

Beglaubigt:

Kanzleiangestellte.

103

Secret State Police
Secret State Police Office
B. Nr. II B-Haftnr. B. 8298   Berlin, SW 11, February 6, 1939
Prinz Albrechtstr. 8

PROTECTIVE CUSTODY ORDER

Christian name and surname: Gottlieb Branz
Date and place of birth: Sept 13, 1896, Munich
Occupation: salesman
Status: married
Nationality: German
Religion: none
Race (only for non-Arians):   Arian
Domicile: Munich, Aignerstr. 32
is to be taken into protective custody.

Reasons:
Police evidence shows that his/her behaviour constitutes a danger to the existence and security of state and people:
Because of his previous activities it is feared that when released, he would continue his illegal Marxist endeavours.

signed: Heydrich
certified:

MILITARY GOVERNMENT OF GERMANY   MG/PS/G/14
Fragebogen für Insassen der Konzentrationslager
CONCENTRATION CAMP INMATES QUESTIONNAIRE

Dachau   13.5.1945
Name des Konzentrationslagers   Datum
Name of Concentration Camp   Date

Ort   Dachau
Location

Name des Lagerinsassen   Maislinger   Adolf
Name of Inmate   Zuname   Vorname
    Last   First   Initial

Geschlecht   male   Geburtsdatum   9.12.03
Sex   Date of Birth

Staatsangehörigkeit   German   without confession
Nationality   Glaubensbekenntnis
    Religion

Wohnungsanschrift   München Oberländerstrasse 15a
Home Address

Beruf   lock-smith
Occupation

Datum der Verhaftung   31.7.4   Durch wen   Gestapo
Date of Arrest   By whom

Ort der Verhaftung   Waldshut a.Rh.
Place of Arrest

Grund für Verhaftung   preparation of high treason
Reason for Arrest

Anklage erhoben   yes
Charge Made

Erkennendes Gericht   Volksger.Berlin 1.Strafsenat
Court Trying Case

Namen der Richter
Names of Judges

Urteil   8 years jail
Sentence

Wo in Haft gewesen und wie lange   31.7.34-42 ...berg and from then K.L.Dachau
Place of Detention Giving Dates

Einzelheiten betreffend die Haft, im besonderen etwaige grausame Behandlung und Zeit derselben. Gründe hierfür und die Namen der Täter, falls bekannt:
Give particulars of confinement including any inhumane treatment with dates, reasons and names of perpetrators, if known:

Stellungen, die Sie während der Haft hatten:
Positions held during confinement:

Haben Sie jemals der NSDAP, deren Gliederungen, angeschlossenen Verbänden oder betreuten Organisationen angehört?
Have you ever belonged to the Nazi Party or any of its affiliated or subordinate organizations?
    never

Falls ja, geben Sie die Organisationen, die Zeit der Mitgliedschaft und die von Ihnen bekleideten Ämter an
If so, list Organizations, dates of membership and positions held:

    Bitte wenden - Please turn

List periods of military service giving organizations and dates as well as ranks held
Geben Sie Ihre Militärdienst unter Angabe der Organisationen, Daten und des Dienstranges an

Geben Sie Tatsachen an, die ihre etwaige Gegnerschaft gegen die Nationalsozialisten erkennen lassen sowie diesbezügliche Tätigkeiten:
List any facts indicating anti-Nazi attitude or activities:
    between 33 and 34 I was arrested several times for the sake of my activity against the Nazi

Geben Sie Ihre Beschäftigung durch Regierungs- und NSDAP-Behörden einschließlich der Art der Beschäftigung und wie Sie diese Anstellung erhalten:
List any employment by governmental or Nazi Party agencies, giving nature of duties and method of appointment:

Waren Sie vom Militärdienst zurückgestellt?   no
Were you deferred from military service?

Wann?   Warum?
When?   Why?

Sind Sie jemals wegen einer strafbaren Handlung verurteilt worden?   never
Wer you ever convicted of any criminal offense?

Falls ja, geben Sie hier in jedem einzelnen Fall Datum, Gericht, Urteil, die strafbare Handlung und das Datum der Haftentlassung:
If so, give date, court, science, offense and date of release in each case:

Wohin beabsichtigen Sie zu gehen, falls Sie aus der Haft entlassen werden?
If released from detention, where do you want to go?

Geben Sie die Namen und die Anschriften dreier vertrauenswürdiger Personen an, die in dem Orte wohnen, wohin Sie gehen wollen und die für Sie bürgen können:
Give names and addresses, if known, of three reliable persons living in the locality where you intend to go, who can vouch for you:

Gezeichnet   Maislinger Adolf adj
Signed

Entscheidung des Ausschusses   Release
Decision of the Board

Endgültige Verfügung betreffend den Lagerinsassen
Final disposal of inmate

Gezeichnet
Signed

    Captain Aus   Vorsitzender des Ausschusses
    Presiding Officer of Board

Rang   Waffengattung   Datum
Rank   Branch   Date

    P.C ormaghtigh Maj STAFF   9.6. - 16.6.45

AUSSCHUSS   Name   Rank   Branch
BOARD   Special Agent CIC

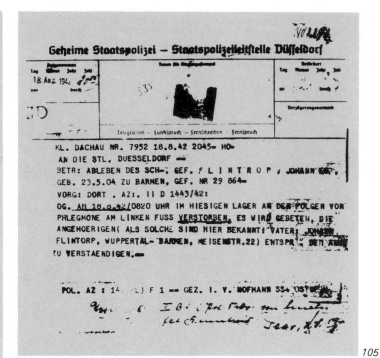

105

Teleprint
Secret State Police–State Police Düsseldorf
August 18, 1942

Dachau concentration camp No. 7952 Aug 17, 1942
To Stl. Düsseldorf
Sub: decease of protective custody prisoner Flintrop, Johann
born: May 23, 1904 in Barmen, Prison No. 29 864–File No. AZ II
D 1443/42
died in this camp on Aug 18, 1942 at 8,20 a. m. as the result of
phlegmone of the left foot.
It is requested that the relatives be informed. (known relatives: father Johann Flintrop, Wuppertal-Barmen, Meisenstr.
22).

104

108

Concentration Camp Dachau	Dachau 3K
Protective Custody Camp	June, 4, 1942

Instructions for Transfer of Prisoners:

Although you are going to be transferred today the camp rules
still apply, therefore you must behave in the place to which
you are taken exactly as you would do in camp. On your return
I shall receive a detailed report on your conduct. Your mail will
be censored from here. You are not allowed to receive packages or visitors. You are not to talk– in a positive or negative
way– about any installations or events in the camp. You are
strictly warned against escape attempts during transportation. Failure to obey these rules will lead to the most stringent
disciplinary measures on your return to camp.

Directives for discharge.

You should show that you are willing to work. In other words, we want to give you the opportunity to integrate completely into the National German community.

You should display your willingness to work for yourselves, your family and the whole German Nation. Noone demands of you that you become National Socialists, leave that to us. We do however demand that you become 100% "Volksgenossen"! You should devote the whole of your energy and skills to your allotted work. All employment is to be accepted even if it is not commensurate with your previous occupation. Unemployment is unknown to us, on the contrary, we do not have enough workers.

Hunger and want do not exist outside. Everyone earns according to his work, and in time each person will be assigned a position for which he is especially suited.

He who finds himself in need through no fault of his own, will be supported by the National Socialist charity organizations (NSW, Wohlfahrt). These organizations are however under no circumstances to be taken advantage of! Relaxation, entertainment and diversion will be provided by the "KdF"—department (strengh through joy). The law makes provision for and protects the right of all workers to take a holiday. However, I wish to warn those who think that they can work against the wishes of the German people, oppose the German people, or flee abroad and from there work against the Germans! We bring everyone back whether it be from another part of the Reich or abroad, and noone escapes our punishment.

The individual is of no concern to us and therefore it is unimportant whether anyone of them stays alive or not. We will achieve the goals which the Führer has set us, despite the endeavours of these parasites. You may speak with noone about the camp, neither positively nor negatively. Noone holds your term of confinement in the concentration camp against you. We forbid you, however, to talk about any camp installations. You are not to establish contact with any former prisoners or to deliver any messages, not even a harmless greeting.

Take these word to heart and act accordingly! If you fail to do so, you will be placed into protective custody again and this time for a period of years not months, and for some there will be no freedom ever again. Re-imprisonment means stricter confinement and you yourselves are best aware of what this means.

Go and work and labour diligently for the welfare of yourselves and your families and thereby for the benefit of the German people and its minorities.

The Reichsführer SS
The Inspector of the Concentration Camps
Pol./Az.: 14 a 14 (cll) L/Ot.   Oranienburg, Dec, 11, 1940

Subject:	Release of prisoners working on essential projects
Reference:	IKL/Pol./Az.: 14a14/L/F from Sept, 7, 1940 and consultation with the Reichssicherheitshauptamt
Enclosures:	-/-

To the Commandants of the Concentration Camps
Da., Sah., Bu., Mau., Flo., Neu., Au., Dirl., FKL Rav., A.L.Gr.-Rosen, We.,
Dept.: assignment of prison labour
copy: Reichssicherheitshauptamt
          Department VI C 2
          Reichskriminalpolizeiamt

In order to avoid difficulties in the replacement of released concentration camp prisoners working on essential projects, it is hereby ordered that the Camp Commandant must inform the Secret State Police or the Reichskriminalpolizeiamt as soon as prisoners are allocated to such work. Apart from personal data (office responsible for admittance, prisoner's number etc.) this information should include a short report as to why an immediate release would be out of the question, together with an indication of the time necessary to train a replacement. Police offices are to take the aforementioned information into consideration when deciding upon the release of prisoners.   signed: Glücks, SS-Oberführer

109

400 Schutzhäftlinge werden aus dem Dachauer Lager entlassen

Aus Anlaß des überwältigenden Sieges des Nationalismus am 12. November und des herannahenden Weihnachtsfriedens hat der polit. Polizeikommandeur Bayerns eine Entlassung von über 500 Schutzhaftgefangenen in ganz Bayern verfügt. Aus dem Konzentrationslager Dachau werden etwa 400 Schutzhäftlinge entlassen. Grundsätzlich werden nur solche Schutzgefangene entlassen, die sich bisher einwandfrei geführt haben und von denen zu erwarten ist, daß sie sich wieder als nützliche Mitglieder der Volksgemeinschaft erweisen werden.
109

107

400 Protective Custody Prisoners are to be released from the Dachau Camp.

On the occasion of National Socialism's enormous victory on November 12, and because of the approaching Christmas holidays, the Chief of the Bavarian political police has ordered the release of more than 500 protective custody prisoners in Bavaria, of which 400 will be released from the Dachau concentration camp. Only those prisoners will be released whose conduct until now has been irreproachable, and of whom it is expected that they will prove themselves to be useful members of society.

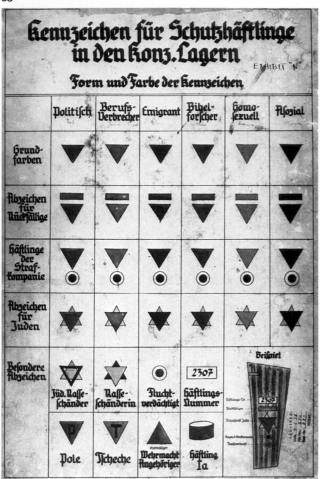

110

Distinguishing symbols worn by prisoners. (table found in the SS-guard room)

The terms used were typical of nazi terminology. Non-German prisoners could be recognized by the letters printed on the triangles on their uniforms.

First there were only political prisoners, Social Democrats, Communists, christian and liberal politicians. Later criminals and so-called "anti-socials" were interned to humiliate the political prisoners.

111
Filing cabinet with prisoners' records

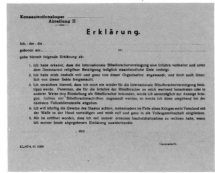

118

Concentration Camp
Department III
Statement

I......, born: ...... in ......
make the following statement:

1. I acknowledge that the International Association of Jehova's Witnesses advocate a false doctrine using their religious activities as a pretext in the pursuit of their subversive aims.
2. I have therefore totally rejected this organization and have freed myself emotionally from the sect.
3. I hereby undertake never again to work for the International Association of Jehova's Witnesses. I shall report any persons who approach me with the false doctrine of Jehova's Witnesses or those who in any way display sympathy for them. Should I receive any Jehova's Witness literature, I shall surrender it immediately to the nearest police station.
4. I shall in future observe the laws of the nation especially in the event of war when I shall take up arms to defend my Fatherland, and strive to become a whole-hearted member of the national community.
5. I have been informed that I must expect a further term of protective custody if I fail to observe the undertaking which I made today.

_____
Signature

119
Gypsies from Burgenland (Austria), Dachau 1938

120

Dachau 1933

121

Dachau 1933

122

123   The youngest of the French prisoners

124

125

126
1934 – prisoners are compelled to listen to a speech by Hitler

127

128 Dachau 1938

Dachau 1938   *129*

Survivors from invalid transports from other camps were first taken to the showers. Flogging the prisoners and hanging them at the stake was also carried out here at times.
130

Disinfection hut for clothing   *131*

132
"Jourhaus" (the guard-room) and entrance to the camp

133

There is one road to freedom.
Its milestones are:
Obedience – diligence – honesty – order – cleanliness – temperance – truth – sacrifice – and love of one's country.

134

Punishment

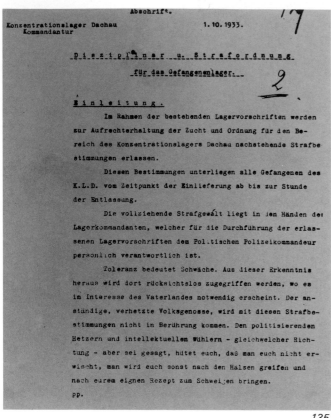

135

Dachau Concentration Camp
Commandant's Office   October 1, 1933

Disciplinary and Penal Code for the Prison Camp

Introduction.

The following penal regulations have been issued within the framework of already existing camp regulations for the maintenance of discipline and order in the Dachau concentration camp.

All prisoners in the Dachau concentration camp are subject to these regulations from the moment they enter until the time of their release.

Executive disciplinary powers are vested in the Commandant, who is personally responsible to the Chief of Political Police for carrying out the prescribed regulations.

Tolerance is a sign of weakness. Therefore action will be taken without consideration, if and where the Nation's interests demand it. The decent citizen who has been incited will not be subjected to punishments laid down in these penal regulations, but let any political or intellectual agitators, whatever their leanings, pay heed: take care that you are not caught or you will be seized by the throat and silenced according to your own prescriptions.

§ 6

A penalty of 8 day's detention and 25 strokes administered before and after the sentence will be given to any person:

1. who makes ironical or jeering remarks to a member of the S.S., who intentionally omits to salute as stipulated, or who by his conduct shows that he does not wish to submit to order and discipline;

2. who as "prisoners' n.c.o.", squad leader or work party leader oversteps the powers of a keeper of public order, arrogates to himself the rights of a superior towards other prisoners, who procures advantages whether at work or otherwise for prisoners who share his views, torments prisoners holding different views from his own, makes false reports about them or injures them in any way.

§ 7

A penalty of 14 days' detention will be given to any person:

1. who on his own authority without orders from the block senior exchanges with another person the quarters assigned to him, or who instigates or inveigles a fellow-prisoner to do so;

2. who encloses in laundry parcels going out of camp articles which are forbidden or manufactured in the camp, or who sews them into laundry, etc.;

3. who enters or leaves huts, living quarters or other buildings other than by the prescribed entrance or climbs through windows or other openings;

4. who smokes in the living quarters, toilets or other places where there is danger of fire, or who places inflamable objects in such places. Cases of fire ensuing from the infringement of this order will be treated as cases of sabotage.

§ 8

A penalty of 14 days' detention and 25 strokes at the beginning and end of the sentence will be given to any person:

1. who leaves or enters the prison camp without escort or without due authority joins any column leaving the camp;

2. who makes unfavourable remarks in letters or other communications about National Socialist leaders, the State or the Government, authorities and institutions, who extols Marxist or liberal leaders or November parties, or who communicates information about events in the camp;

3. who keeps forbidden articles, tools, cutting or thrusting weapons in his quarters or sleeping bag.

§ 9

A penalty of 21 days' detention will be given to any person who removes from its prescribed locality, damages intentionally, destroys, wastes, alters or uses for other purposes than those prescribed, articles of any sort belonging to the State. In addition to any punishment, the individual or whole group of prisoners will, according to the circumstances, be held indemnifiable for damage caused.

§ 10

A penalty of 42 days' detention or prolonged solitary confinement will be given to any person:

1. who collects sums of money within the camp, who finances forbidden intrigues either inside or outside, or who gives money to fellow prisoners to act for him or to buy their silence;

2. who has money from collections of the "Rote Hilfe" sent to him or who distributes it to fellow prisoners;

3. who communicates to a priest information other than spiritual, passes letters to him to be forwarded or seeks to prevail upon him for forbidden purposes;

4. who vilifies the emblems of the National Socialist State or those who wear them, insults them or disregards them in any other way.

§ 11

Any person, who at work, in the living quarters, kitchen, workshops, toilets or rest places engages in subversive politics, holds provocative speeches, congregates with others for this purpose,, forms cliques, loiters, collects, receives or buries information, repeats or smuggles out of the camp by means of a note or some other method to a camp visitor information, either true or false, concerning the camp, to be used in our enemies horror propaganda, or who sends written or verbal message through released or transferred prisoners, conceals them in items of clothing or other objects, throws them over the wall, writes coded messages, or any person who in order to incite rebellion climbs onto the roof of the huts or up trees, or transmits signals with a lamp or by any other means, seeks outside contact, or advises, supports or aids others in escape or crime, will be hanged as a subversive instigator under the terms of the revolutionary law.

§ 13

Any person who in the camp, in living quarters, workshops, kitchen, stores etc. deliberately causes a fire, explosion, flooding or any other material damage, or any person who tampers in any way which does not correspond to orders given, with the barbed-wire fence, high-tension cables, electricity junction boxes, telephone lines, water pipes, the walls of the camp or other security installations, heating installations or boilers, engines or motor vehicles, will be punished by death as a saboteur.

If the deed is committed through negligence the guilty party will be placed in solitary confinement.

Doubtful cases will be treated as sabotage.

§ 19

Solitary confinement consists of a diet of water and dry bread and a hard bed. The prisoner will be given hot food every 4 days. Hard labour includes hard physical and especially dirty work carried out under strict surveillance.

The following complementary punishments are laid down: Punishment drill, flogging, deprivation of mail, withdrawal of food, hard bed, the "post", reprimands and warning.

All punishments will be recorded in the prisoner's personal file. Detention and hard labour will prolong preventive dentention by at least 4 weeks. Prisoners in cells cannot be released from the camp within the foreseeable future.

The Concentration Camp Commandant
(L.S.)

signed: Eicke
SS-Oberführer

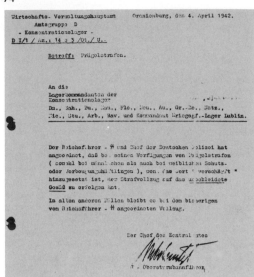

136

Wirtschaftsverwaltungshauptamt
Amtsgruppe D
–Concentration Camps–
D I/1 Az: 14 s 3/Ot/U.   Oranienburg, April 4, 1942

To the Commandants of the Concentration Camps

Da. Sah. Bu. Mau. Flo. Neu. Au. Gr.Ro. Natz. Nie, Stu.
Arb. Rav und Kommandant Kriegsgef. Lager Lublin

According to the instructions of the Reichsführer SS and
Chief of the German Police regarding flogging (both for
male and female protective custody and preventive custody prisoners) if the word "stringent" is included in the
order, it is to be administered on unclothed buttocks.
All other cases are to be dealt with in accordance with
the previous instructions of the Reichsführer SS.

Chief of the Central Office
SS-Obersturmbannführer

Whipping-block   137

SS-Wirtschaftsverwaltungshauptamt
Amtsgruppe D
D I/1Az: 14 e 3/0/S.—   Oranienburg, Oct, 13, 1943

Subject: ·   Flogging of French prisoners
Reference: The Chief of the Sipo and the SD
                    IV D 4 2295/43 of oct 6, 1943
Enclosures: none

To the Commandants of the Concentration Camps
Da., Sah., Bu., Mau., Flo., Neu., Au., Gr.Ro., Natz., Ri., Stu., Lub., Rav., AL. Berg.Belsen.

In agreement with the Chief of the Security Police and the SD the flogging of French prisoners is to be stopped as this would probably be exploited for negative propaganda purposes after the prisoners' release.

I therefore request that in the case of French prisoners flogging be replaced by an alternative camp punishment.

SS-Obersturmbannführer

138

139 The punishments consisted of deprival of food, standing on the parade ground, extra work, punishment drill, transfer to the punishment company, transfer to a more stringent work detail, beating (stick or whip), suspension by the wrists from a tree or pole, solitary confinement, beating to death, hanging, shooting, and a host of specially selected tortures.

Eugen Kogon, Der SS-Staat

140
Buchenwald

Punishment company 141

Prisoners who were admitted to the camp a second time or who had been sentenced by the Gestapo to custody with harsher conditions were strictly isolated from the rest of the camp in three barrack huts.

Although they were made to do more strenuous work than the other prisoners they were given less food.

143

Notification

As I have once again acted in a manner detrimental to the State and nation I had to be taken into protective custody for a second time which means that I am to be subjected to a more stringent confinement.
1. I may receive and write only one letter per quarter.
2. I may only receive 10 Marks per quarter.
3. I am forbidden to receive any parcels whatsoever.
                signed: Robert Eisinger

142

Dachau, d. 4.X.1937

Mitteilung.

Da ich mich erneut gegen Volk und Staat im staatsfeinlichem Sinne betätigt habe und daher zum 2.mal in Schutzhaft genommen werden mußte, unterliege ich den verschärften Haftmaßnahmen.
1. Ich darf im 1/4 Jahr nur einen Brief empfangen und schreiben.
2. Ich darf im 1/4 Jahr nur 10 RM. empfangen,
3. Der Empfang jeglicher Pakete ist verboten.

Robert Eisinger

144 Camp prison ("Bunker"), prison yard and wall where many prisoners were shot

145 Standing torture

SS-Head Office for Economic Organization

146

ϟϟ-Wirtschafts-Verwaltungshauptamt

Chef: ϟϟ-Gruppenführer und Generalleutnant der Waffen-ϟϟ POHL
Vertreter: ϟϟ-Brigadeführer und Generalmajor der Waffen-ϟϟ FRANK

Adjutantur
Persönliches Büro
Gerichts- und Fürsorgeführer
Wirtschaftsprüfer
Betriebsinspekteur | Deutsche Wirtschaftsbetriebe GmbH.
Haupteingangsstelle
Hauskommandant
Archiv

Geheim

Nur für den Dienstgebrauch.
Veröffentlichung untersagt!

Department A troop administration	Department B troop economy	Department C building projects	Department D concentration camps	Department E economic enterprises
Chef: ϟϟ-Brigadeführer, Generalmajor der Waffen-ϟϟ Frank	Chef: ϟϟ-Brigadeführer, Generalmajor der Waffen-ϟϟ Lörner	Chef: ϟϟ-Oberführer Dr. Ing. Kammler	Chef: ϟϟ-Brigadeführer, Generalmajor der Waffen-ϟϟ Glücks	Chef: ϟϟ-Gruppenführer Pohl
Vertreter: ϟϟ-Standartenführer Fanslau	Vertreter: ϟϟ-Standartenführer Prietzel	Vertreter: ϟϟ-Sturmbannführer Busching	Vertreter: ϟϟ-Oberführer Liebehenschel	Vertreter: ϟϟ-Brigadeführer Lörner
Adjutant und Kompaniechef: ϟϟ-Hauptsturmführer Solleder	Adjutant und Kompaniechef: ϟϟ-Obersturmführer Maurahberger	Adjutant und Kompaniechef: ϟϟ-Obersturmführer Pastowsky	Adjutant: ϟϟ-Hauptsturmführer Harbaum	
Amt A I: Haushaltsamt	**Amt B I:** Verpflegungswirtschaft	**Amt C I:** Allgemeine Bauaufgaben	**Amt D I:** Zentralamt	**Amt W I:** Steine und Erden (Reich)
ϟϟ-Standartenführer Lörner	ϟϟ-Standartenführer Prietzel	ϟϟ-Sturmbannführer Sesemann	ϟϟ-Obersturmbannführer Liebehenschel	ϟϟ-Sturmbannführer Mummenthey
A I 1: Haushalt der Waffen-ϟϟ		C I 1: Bauten der Waffen-ϟϟ	D I 1: Häftlingsangelegenheiten	W I 1: Deutsche Erd- und Steinwerke GmbH. 4 Großziegeleien
A I 2: Haushalt der Allg.-ϟϟ Reichskassenverwalter	B I 1: Planung und Beschaffung der Verpflegung für Mann und Pferd	C I 2: Bauten der K.L. und Kriegsgefangenenlager	D I 2: Nachrichtenwesen	W I 2: Deutsche Erd- und Steinwerke GmbH. 6 Steinbrüche
A I 3: Spargemeinschaft	B I 2: Truppen-Wirtschafts-Lager	C I 3: Bauten der Deutschen Polizei	D I 3: Lagerschutz- und Wachhunde	W I 3: Porzellan-Manufaktur Allach GmbH.
	B I 3: Versuche und Nahrungsmittelprüfung, Ausbildung der Köche, Lehrküchen	C I 4: Bauten der Allgemeinen-ϟϟ	D I 4: Waffen und Geräte	Bohemia — Keramische Werke A. G.
Amt A II: Kassen und Besoldungswesen			D I 5: Schulung der Truppe	„Porag" — Porzellan Radiatoren GmbH.
ϟϟ-Obersturmbannführer Eggert		**Amt C II:** Sonderbauaufgaben		Victoria-Porzellan A.G.
A II 1: Besoldungswesen	**Amt B II:** Bekleidungswirtschaft	ϟϟ-Sturmbannführer Kiefer	**Amt D II:** Arbeitseinsatz der Häftlinge	**Amt W II:** Steine und Erden (Ost)
A II 2: Kassen- und Rechnungswesen	ϟϟ-Sturmbannführer Lechler	C II/1: Verpflegungs- und Bekleidungsbauten	ϟϟ-Sturmbannführer Maurer	ϟϟ-Sturmbannführer Dr. Bobermin
A II 3: Gebührenstelle		C II/2: Waffen-, Munitions- und Nachrichtenbauten		W II 1: Ostdeutsche Baustoffwerke GmbH. 292 Ziegeleien
	B II 1: Bekleidung und Ausrüstung für Mann und Führer	C II/3: Lazarette und Reviere	D II/1: Häftlingseinsatz	W II 2: Generaltreuhänder für Baustofferzeugungsstätten mit Gaue Steiermark und Kärnten 18 Betriebe
Amt A III: Rechtsamt	B II/2: ϟϟ-Bekleidungswerke	C II/4: Nationalpolitische Erziehungsanstalten und Heimschulen	D II/2: Häftlingsausbildung	W II 3: Rußlandbetriebe
ϟϟ-Brigadeführer und Generalmajor der Waffen-ϟϟ Frank	B II/3: ϟϟ-Kleiderkasse	C II/5: Wohnungsfürsorge	D II/3: Statistik und Verrechnung	
A III 1: Allgemeine Rechts-, Steuer- und Vertragsangelegenheiten		C II 6: Wirtschafts- und Sonderbauten		**Amt W III:** Ernährungsbetriebe
A III 2: Grundstücks- und Gebäudekataster	**Amt B III:** Unterkunftswirtschaft		**Amt D III:** Sanitätswesen und Lagerhygiene	ϟϟ-Oberführer Möckel
	ϟϟ-Obersturmbannführer Köberlein	**Amt C III:** Technische Fachgebiete	ϟϟ-Obersturmbannführer Dr. Lolling	W III 1: Sudetenquell GmbH. Heinr. Mattoni A. G.
Amt A IV: Prüfungsamt		ϟϟ-Sturmbannführer Wirtz		W III 2: Rheinahr Glasfabrik GmbH.
ϟϟ-Obersturmbannführer Vogt	B III/1: Planung und Beschaffung der Unterkunftsgeräte	C III/1: Ingenieurbau	D III/1: Ärztliche und zahnärztliche Versorgung der ϟϟ	W III 2: Freudenthaler Getränke GmbH.
A IV 1: Prüfung des Kassen- und Rechnungswesens	B III/2: Unterkunftslager	C III/2: Be- und Entwässerung	D III/2: Ärztliche und zahnärztliche Versorgung der Häftlinge	W III 3: Deutsche Lebensmittel GmbH.
A IV 2: Prüfung der truppenwirtschaftlichen Einrichtungen (Truppen-Wirtschaftslager, Bekl. Werke u. a.)	B III/3: Kraftfahrwesen für Amtsgruppen A und B einschl. Wirtschafts-Lager	C III/3: Maschinenbau	D III/3: Hygienische und sanitäre Maßnahmen in den K.L.	**Amt W IV:** Holzbearbeitungsbetriebe
		C III/4: Vermessung		ϟϟ-Hauptsturmführer Dr. May
Amt A V: Personalamt	**Amt B IV:** Rohstoffe und Beschaffungen	**Amt C IV:** Künstlerische Fachgebiete	**Amt D IV:** KL-Verwaltung	W IV 1: Deutsche Ausrüstungswerke GmbH. 6 Werke
ϟϟ-Standartenführer Fanslau	ϟϟ-Obersturmbannführer Weggel	ϟϟ-Sturmbannführer (S) Blaschek	ϟϟ-Obersturmbannführer Kaindl	W IV 2: Deutsche Heimgestaltung GmbH. 13 Werke
A V 1: Ersatz, Erlassung, Entlassungen		C IV/1: Städtebau- und Entwurfsgestaltung	D IV/1: Haushalt, Kassen- und Beschäftigungswesen	W IV 3: Deutsche Meisterwerkstätten GmbH. 1 Werk
A V 2: Beförderungen, Kommandierungen, Versetzungen	B IV/1: Rohstoffe (Textil und Leder)	C IV/2: Landschafts- und Raumgestaltung	D IV/2: Verpflegung	
A V 3: Ausbildung und Schulen	B IV/2: Beschaffung von Bekleidung		D IV/3: Bekleidung	**Amt W V:** Land-, Forst-, Fischwirtschaft
A V 4: K.L.: Ersatz, Entlassungen, Beförderungen, Kommandierungen, Versetzungen, Ausbildung (der Amtgr. D zugeteilt).	B IV/3: Preisprüfwesen	**Amt C V:** Zentrale Bauinspektion	D IV/4: Unterkunft	ϟϟ-Sturmbannführer Vogel
	B IV/4: Auftragsverlagerung Beschaffungen im Ausland	ϟϟ-Obersturmbannführer Lenzer	D IV/5: Rechts-, Steuer- und Vertragsangelegenheiten	W V 1: Deutsche Versuchsanstalt für Ernährung und Verpflegung GmbH. 30 Betriebe
		C V/1: Dienstaufsicht über die Baudienststellen und Bauvorhaben		W V 2: Forstwesen 10 Betriebe
		C V/2: Haushalt und Rechnungslegung		W V 3: Fischwirtschaft 16 Betriebe
		C V/3: Rohstoffstelle Bau und Baulager		
		C V/4: Kraftfahrwesen für Amtgruppe C		**Amt W VI:** Textil- und Lederverwertung
				ϟϟ-Sturmbannführer Lechler
		Amt C VII: Bauunterhaltung und Betriebswirtschaft		W VI 1: Gesellschaft für Textil- und Lederverwertung GmbH.
		ϟϟ-Standartenführer Eirenschmalz		
		C VII/1: Liegenschaften der Waffen-ϟϟ		**Amt W VII:** Buch und Bild
		C VII/2: Liegenschaften der Allg.-ϟϟ		ϟϟ-Hauptsturmführer Dr. Mischke
		C VII/3: Verpflegungsstelle für das Bauwesen		W VII 1: Nordland-Verlag GmbH
				W VII 2: Deutscher Bilderdienst
				Amt W VIII: Sonderaufgaben
				ϟϟ-Sturmbannführer Klein
				W VIII/1: Gesellschaft zur Pflege und Förderung deutscher Kulturdenkmäler e. V.
				W VIII/2: Externsteine-Stiftung e. V. König, Heinrich-Gedächtnis-Stiftung e. V.
				W VIII/3: Genesungs- und Erholungsheime Kulturbauten

Genehmigt!
Führerhauptquartier, den 3. März 1942
gez. H. Himmler.

ϟϟ-EWO 74. 660 3. 42.

149 Women guards in the Bergen-Belsen concentration camp

147 SS-guards

148 SS road sign

150 SS-dining hall
151 Commandant of Dachau with SS-officers

152

153

Monthly National Socialist Review
"Freedom and Bread"
Central political and cultural periodical of the NSDAP No 46

SA and SS

Contents:
Rudolf Hess, SA and the Party–Ernst Röhm, The Brown Batall-
ions of the German Revolution–Heinrich Himmler, The Task of
the SS–Ernst Röhm, Why the SA–Otto Dietrich, The Struggle
of the heroic ideology (Weltanschauung)–Hajo von Hadeln,
The Student and the SA–Gunther d'Alquen, The Conscience
of the National Socialist Revolution–German Poetry–German
Prose–Waldemar Hartmann, Burgos, the City of El Cid–Contemporary Criticism–The Book.

Reichsführer S.S. Heinrich Himmler:

Die Aufgabe der S.S.

„Wir schwören Dir — Adolf Hitler — Treue und Tapferkeit. — Wir
geloben Dir — und den von Dir bestimmten Vorgesetzten — Gehorsam bis
in den Tod. — So wahr uns Gott helfe."
Mit diesem Eid wurden die Standarte „Adolf Hitler" und sämtliche Ab-
schnitts- und Gruppenführer der S.S. am 9. November 1933 auf den Führer
verpflichtet.

THE TASK OF THE "SS"

154

To you, Adolf Hitler, we swear our allegiance and resolute-
ness. We solemnly pledge to you and to the superiors appointed by you, our obedience unto death. So help us God.
On 9 November, 1933, the Standarte "Adolf Hitler" and all unit
and group leaders of the SS pledged themselves to the Führer
with this oath.
We see before us a most urgent task: to uncover, combat and
destroy all confessed and secret enemies of the Führer, the
National Socialist Movement and our national revolution.

Germany, nothing but Germany!

155

. . . On September 29, 1933 I was commissioned to the SS
liaison staff in Passau after the dissolution of which I was detailed to the Austrian SS in the Dachau camp on Jan 29, 1934.
On October 1, 1934 I was ordered to take up duties in the Main
office of the Security Service where I have since carried out my
duties to the present day.

Adolf Eichmann

Himmler in Dachau

157

158

159

160

156
Agenda of a
meeting of high-ranking
SS officers in Dachau

161

SS-Careers which began in Dachau...

NAME	IN DACHAU	IN ANDEREN LAGERN ODER SS-FUNKTIONEN		
AUMEIER, Johann	Schutzhaftlagerführer Kommandant (Aussenlager Kaufering) 1944/45	SACHSENHAUSEN FLOSSENBÜRG: AUSCHWITZ:	Schutzhaftlagerführer Schutzhaftlagerführer	1936 1938/42 1942/43
BAER, Karl Richard	Angehöriger der Wachtruppe 1933/34	COLUMBIA HAUS: NEUENGAMME: SS-WVHA: AUSCHWITZ: DORA:	Adjutant d. Kommandanten Adjutant Kommandant Kommandant	1934 1942 1942/43 1944 1945
BARANOWSKI, Hermann	Schutzhaftlagerführer 1936/38	SACHSENHAUSEN:	Kommandant	1938/40
EICHMANN, Adolf	Unterscharführer (SS-Ausbildungslager) 1934	SD Hauptamt: Gestapo: Gestapo, Amt IV:	Referent f. jüdische Fragen Abteilungsleiter	1934 1939 1941/45
EICKE, Theodor	Kommandant 1933/34	Inspekteur aller Konzentrationslager		1934-39
FRITZSCH, Karl	Schutzhaftlagerführer 1934/40	AUSCHWITZ: FLOSSENBÜRG: DORA:	Schutzhaftlagerführer Kommandant	1940/41 1943/44
GRÜNEWALD, Adam	Schutzhaftlagerführer 1938/39	LICHTENBURG: BUCHENWALD: SACHSENHAUSEN: HERZOGENBUSCH:	Angehöriger d. Wachtruppe Schutzhaftlagerführer Kommandant	1934 1938 1942 1943/44
HÖSS, Rudolf	Blockführer, Rapportführer 1934/38	SACHSENHAUSEN: AUSCHWITZ: SS-WVHA:	Schutzhaftlagerführer, Adjutant d. Kommandanten Kommandant Chef des Amtes D I (Politische Abteilung d. Inspektion d. Konzentrationslager)	1938/40 1940/43 1943/45
HOFMANN, Franz Josef	Angehöriger d. Wachtruppe 1933 Rapportführer 1933/37 Schutzhaftlagerführer 1941/42	AUSCHWITZ: NATZWEILER:	Schutzhaftlagerführer Schutzhaftlagerführer	1942/44 1944
KOEGEL, Max	Schutzhaftlagerführer, Adjutant d. Kommandanten 1937/38	COLUMBIA HAUS: LICHTENBURG: RAVENSBRÜCK: LUBLIN: FLOSSENBÜRG:	Adjutant d. Kommandanten Schutzhaftlagerführer Kommandant Kommandant Kommandant	1936 1938 1940 1942 1943/45

NAME	IN DACHAU
KRAMER, Josef	Kommandantur 1937 Schulung zum Lagerführer 1940/
LORITZ, Hans	Kommandant 1936/ SACH
REMMELE, Josef	Angehöriger der Wachtruppe 1934/ Blockführer 1936 Arbeitsdienst 1937/ Blockführer 1941/42
SCHWARZHUBER, Johann	Rapportführer
THUMANN, Anton	Rapportführer
TRENKLE, Franz Xaver	Blockführer 1933/ Kommandoführer 1936/ stellv. Schutzhaftlagerführer 1942/
WEISS, Martin Gottfried	Techn. Leiter 1933/ Adjutant d. Kommanda 1938/ Kommandant 1942/
ZILL, Egon	2. Schutzhaftlagerführer 1937 1. Schutzhaftlagerführer 1939/

ANDEREN LAGERN ODER SS-FUNKTIONEN

TERWEGEN:	Kommandantur	1935/36
CHSENHAUSEN:	Adjutantur; Post	1937/38
UTHAUSEN:	Adjutant d. Kommandanten	1938/40
SCHWITZ:	Adjutant d. Kommandanten	1940
TZWEILER:	Schutzhaftlagerführer,	
	Kommandant	1941/44
SCHWITZ-		
RKENAU	Kommandant	1944
RGEN-BELSEN:	Kommandant	1944/45

TERWEGEN:	Kommandant	1934/36
CHSENHAUSEN:	Kommandant	1940/42

SCHWITZ
ommando Eintrachtshütte)
SCHWITZ
ommando Jawischowitz): Schutzhaftlager-
führer

CHSENHAUSEN:	Angehöriger d. Wachtruppe	1938/42
SCHWITZ		
RKENAU:	Schutzhaftlagerführer	1944
VENSBRÜCK:	Schutzhaftlagerführer	1945

TERWEGEN:	Schutzhaftlagerführer	
OSS-ROSEN		1941/43
BLIN:	Schutzhaftlagerführer	1943/44
UENGAMME:		1944/45
SCHWITZ-		
RKENAU:	Schutzhaftlagerführer	

UENGAMME:	Rapportführer	1939/41
CHSENHAUSEN:	Kommandoführer	1941/42
RGEN-BELSEN:	Schutzhaftlagerführer	1944

UENGAMME;	Kommandant	1940/42
BLIN;	Kommandant	1943/44
WVHA:	Chef, Amtsgruppe D	
	z.b.V. (Konzentrationslager)	1944/5

HTENBURG:	Angehöriger d. Wachtruppe,	
	Schutzhaftlagerführer	1934/37
CHENWALD:	19	1937/38
VENSBRÜCK:		1939
NZERT:	Kommandant	1942
TZWEILER:	Kommandant	1942/43
OSSENBÜRG:	Kommandant	1943

SS-camp in Dachau

SS-barracks

Reports in the "politically coordinated" German press, 1933

165

167

Bavarian Prime Minister in Dachau.

A letter from the Bavarian Prime Minister to the SS leader Himmler regarding conditions in the Dachau concentration camp:
This week the Prime Minister made a thorough inspection of the various departments and facilities of the Dachau concentration camp. He also inspected the premises and facilities of the Political and Security Police. As a result of what he saw he wrote a letter to the Commander of the Political Police reaffirming that the tales which one hears from time to time about conditions in the Dachau camp are completely unfounded.

168

Local News   166

Dachau-Indersdorf

169

New Commandant—The Chief of the 1st Sturmbann of the 56th SS Standarte—Norbert Scharf has been appointed Concentration Camp Commandant.

HANS BEIMLER
MITGLIED DES REICHSTAGS
POLITISCHER LEITER DER KPD
SÜDBAYERNS

IM MÖRDERLAGER
DACHAU

VIER WOCHEN IN DEN HÄNDEN DER
BRAUNEN BANDITEN

1933
VERLAGSGENOSSENSCHAFT AUSLÄNDISCHER
ARBEITER IN DER UdSSR / MOSKAU-LENINGRAD

173

**FOUR WEEKS
in the Hands
OF HITLER'S
Hell-Hounds**

THE NAZI
MURDER
CAMP OF
DACHAU

By HANS BEIMLER
Member of the Reichstag: Leader of the
Southern Bavarian District. Communist
Party of Germany

3ᵈ

MODERN   BOOKS   LTD

172

Konzentrationslager

Ein Appell an das Gewissen der Welt

Ein Buch der Greuel
Die Opfer klagen an

DACHAU — BRANDENBURG — PAPENBURG
KÖNIGSTEIN — LICHTENBURG — COLDITZ
SACHSENBURG — MORINGEN — HOHNSTEIN
REICHENBACH — SONNENBURG

VERLAGSANSTALT »GRAPHIA«, KARLSBAD 1934

171

170

Thursday   Arbeiter Zeitung (Workers' News) Jan 4

50 Murdered in Dachau

London, January 3, The Manchester Guardian reports on the Dachau
concentration camp:

The 2200 to 2400 internees are accommodated in 10 barrack huts.
They include 50 intellectuals, a few members of the middle class, 50
or 60 Nazis, approximately 500 social democrats, 2 officers, several
criminals, and 15 foreigners, the rest being communists. The majority of the prisoners are of the working class.
The prisoners are organized in 10 companies each with a maximum
of 270 men. Number 7 is the disciplinary company, number 1 is
composed of social democrats and communist workers, and
number 2 consists of Jews. Communist functionaries refusing to
give the Nazis political information are locked in cells. The cells are
damp, dark, and without heating. The prisoners are chained to the
walls; crude wooden planks serve as beds. In September the prisoners were made to build 21 new cells.
Corporal punishment is practiced in Dachau. The prisoners are flog-
ged with wire-bound whips which they have to make themselves.
They receive 25 to 75 heavy lashes.
On entry to the camp communists and social democrats are beaten
for no apparent reason. The prisoners are also beaten with wet to-
wels. Seven SA-men, brought to the camp on August 1, were so ill-
treated that two of them, Amuschel and Handschuch, died as a result. The communist Fritz Schaper was ill-treated in such a way that
he was unable to move for two months. On September 2, a Nazi
guard struck one of the prisoners, thereby breaking his jaw.
The prisoners are also often burned with lighted cigarettes.
Among those suffering the most terrible treatment are L. Buchmann,
Georg Freischütz und the journalist Ewald Thunig. The Munich
communist, Sepp Götz, was murdered after being so severely ill-
treated that he could no longer stand. The student Wickelmeier was
shot. The communist, Fritz Dressel, died as a result of ill-treatment.
Town councillor Hausmann, Lehrburger, the "Reichsbanner"-man
Aron, Willi Franz, and Buerk, a communist functionary from Mem-
mingen, were killed: a total of nearly 50 men.
The correspondent of the Manchester Guardian is in possession of
the names of 9 guards who ill-treat and murder prisoners.

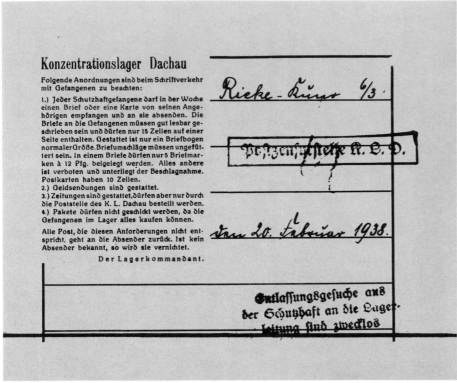

174

175

Concentration Camp Dachau

The following regulations are to be observed by those corresponding with prisoners:

1. Protective custody prisoners may receive and reply to one letter or postcard from their relatives every three months. These letters must be legible and written in ink with a maximum of 15 lines per page. One sheet of writing paper of normal size is allowed. Unlined envelopes must be used. Only two 12pfennig stamps may be enclosed in each letter. Anything else is forbidden and will be confiscated.
2. Postcards are to have a maximum of 10 lines and photos are not to be used as postcards.
3. A maximum of 10 Reichmarks may be sent every 3 months.
4. Newspapers are not allowed.
5. Parcels may not be sent as the prisoners can buy everything in the camp.

All mail which does not meet with these requirements will be returned to the sender. If the sender is not known, the mail will be destroyed.

Dachau 3 K, Sept 5, 1944

Directive.

To be included in the next quarterly letter:

1) There is no limit to the number of parcels which a prisoner may receive. Only foodstuffs which are suitable for immediate consumption may be sent.

2) Both the sender and the recipient will be punished if parcels are used to smuggle letters, money, notes, tools or other forbidden articles including pictures.

3) From now on the sending of sealed registered letters or express goods to prisoners is forbidden.

No quarterly letter may be sent without this final clause. This text is to be included in the following two quarterly letters in the case of new admissions.

The Chief of the Protective
Custody Camp
SS Obersturmbannführer

176

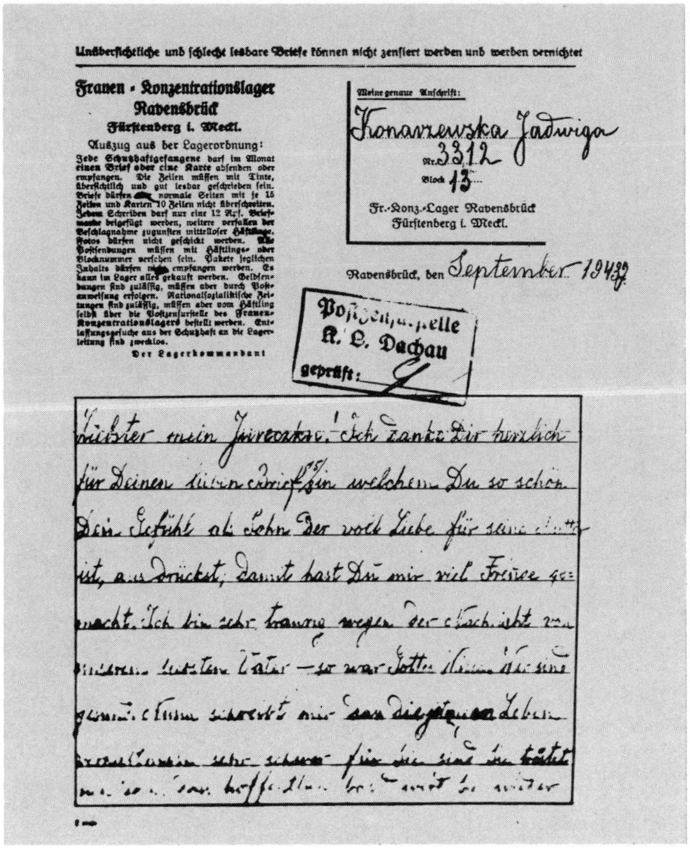

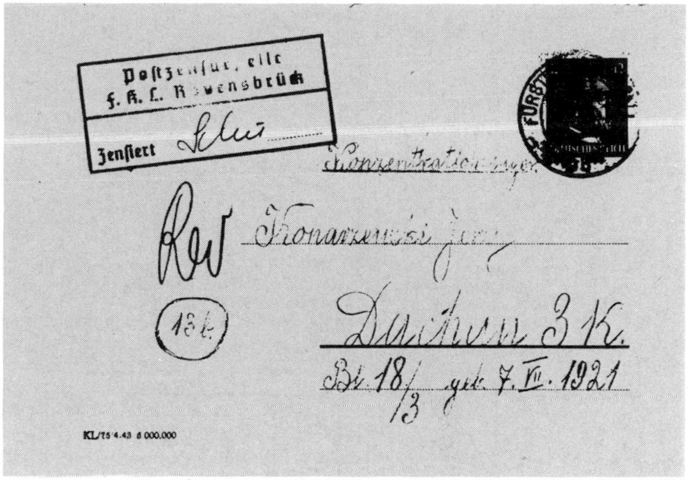

Unübersichtliche und schlecht lesbare Briefe können nicht zensiert werden und werden vernichtet

Frauen - Konzentrationslager Ravensbrück
Fürstenberg i. Meckl.

Auszug aus der Lagerordnung:
Jede Schutzhaftgefangene darf im Monat einen Brief oder eine Karte absenden oder empfangen. Die Zeilen müssen mit Tinte, übersichtlich und gut lesbar geschrieben sein. Briefe dürfen [illegible] normale Seiten mit je 15 Zeilen und Karten 10 Zeilen nicht überschreiten. Jedem Schreiben darf nur eine 12 Rpf. Briefmarke beigefügt werden, weitere verfallen der Beschlagnahme zugunsten mittelloser Häftlinge. Fotos dürfen nicht geschickt werden. Alle Postsendungen müssen mit Häftlings- oder Blocknummer versehen sein. Pakete jeglichen Inhalts dürfen nicht empfangen werden. Es kann im Lager alles gekauft werden. Geldsendungen sind zulässig, müssen aber durch Postanweisung erfolgen. Nationalsozialistische Zeitungen sind zulässig, müssen aber vom Häftling selbst über die Postzensurstelle des Frauen-Konzentrationslagers bestellt werden. Entlassungsgesuche aus der Schutzhaft an die Lagerleitung sind zwecklos.

Der Lagerkommandant

Meine genaue Anschrift:
Konarzewska Jadwiga
Nr. 3312
Block 13
Fr.-Konz.-Lager Ravensbrück
Fürstenberg i. Meckl.

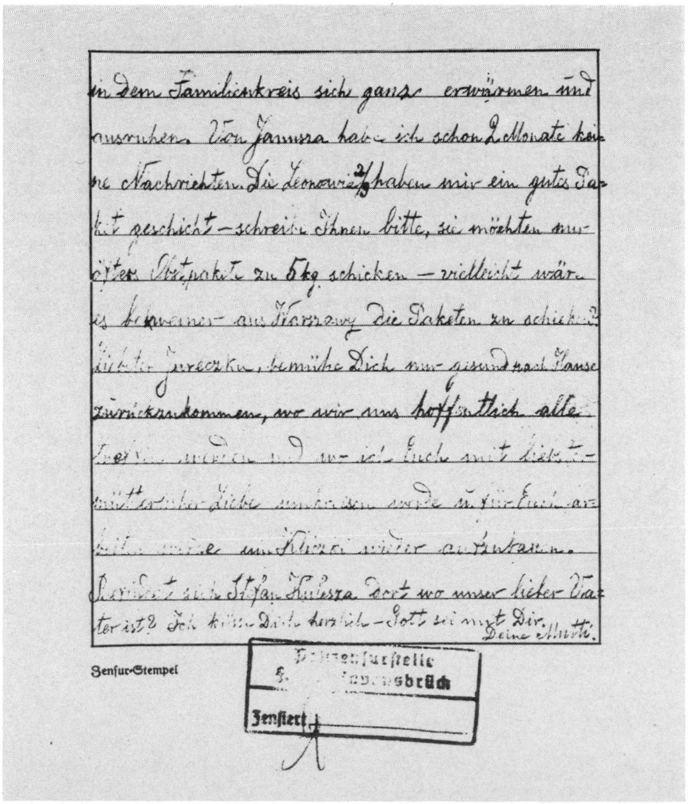

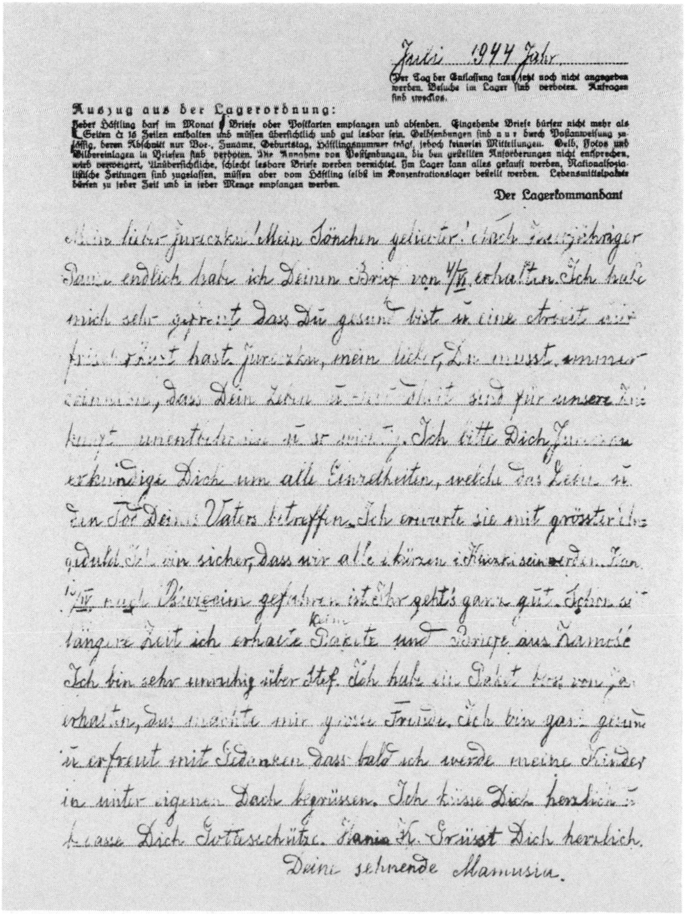

Ravensbrück, den September 1943

Postzensurstelle
K. L. Dachau
geprüft:

Liebster mein Jureczko! Ich danke Dir herzlich
für Deinen lieben Brief, in welchem Du so schön
Dein Gefühl als Sohn der voll Liebe für seine Mutti
ist, ausdrückst; damit hast Du mir viel Freude gemacht. Ich bin sehr traurig wegen der Nachricht von
unserem liebsten Vater – so war Gottes [illegible]
[illegible] schreibt mir [illegible] Leben
[illegible] sehr schwer [illegible]
[illegible]

in dem Familienkreis sich ganz erwärmen und
ausruhen. Von Janusz habe ich schon 2 Monate keine Nachrichten. Die Leonowicz haben mir ein gutes Paket geschickt – schreibe Ihnen bitte, sie möchten mir
öfter Obstpakete zu 5 kg schicken – vielleicht wäre
es bequemer aus Warszawy die Paketen zu schicken.
Liebster Jureczko, bemühe Dich nur gesund nach Hause
zurückzukommen, wo wir uns hoffentlich alle
[illegible] und wo ich Euch mit [illegible]
mütterlicher Liebe umarmen werde [illegible]
[illegible]
[illegible] sich Stefan Kulesza dort wo unser lieber Vater ist? Ich küsse Dich herzlich – Gott sei mit Dir.
Deine Mutti.

Zensur-Stempel

Postzensurstelle
[illegible] Ravensbrück
Zensiert

A mother interned in Ravensbrück women's concentration camp writes to her son in Dachau concentration camp.
All prisoners–even Non-Germans were forced to write in German.

177

Postzensurstelle
F. K. L. Ravensbrück
Zensiert

Konzentrationslager
Konarzewski Jerzy
Dachau 3 K.
Bl. 18/3 geb. 7. VII. 1921

KL/15 4.43 6 000.000

Juli 1944 Jahr

Der Tag der Entlassung kann jetzt noch nicht angegeben werden. Besuche im Lager sind verboten. Anfragen sind zwecklos.

Auszug aus der Lagerordnung:
Jeder Häftling darf im Monat [illegible] Briefe oder Postkarten empfangen und absenden. Eingehende Briefe dürfen nicht mehr als [illegible] Seiten à 15 Zeilen enthalten und müssen übersichtlich und gut lesbar sein. Geldsendungen sind nur durch Postanweisung zulässig, deren Abschnitt nur Vor-, Zuname, Geburtstag, Häftlingsnummer trägt, jedoch keinerlei Mitteilungen. Geld, Fotos und Bildereinlagen in Briefen sind verboten. Die Annahme von Postsendungen, die den gestellten Anforderungen nicht entsprechen, wird verweigert. Unübersichtliche, schlecht lesbare Briefe werden vernichtet. Im Lager kann alles gekauft werden. Nationalsozialistische Zeitungen sind zugelassen, müssen aber vom Häftling selbst im Konzentrationslager bestellt werden. Lebensmittelpakete dürfen zu jeder Zeit und in jeder Menge empfangen werden.

Der Lagerkommandant

Mein lieber Jureczku! Mein Söhnchen geliebter! Nach [illegible]
[illegible] endlich habe ich Deinen Brief von 4/VI. erhalten. Ich habe
mich sehr gefreut dass Du gesund bist [illegible]
[illegible] hast Jureczku, mein lieber, Du musst immer
[illegible], dass Dein Leben [illegible] sind für unsere Zukunft [illegible] so wichtig. Ich bitte Dich, Jureczku
erkundige Dich um alle Einzelheiten, welche das Leben und
den Tod Deines Vaters betreffen. Ich erwarte sie mit grösster Un-
geduld. Ich bin sicher, dass wir alle in kürzen [illegible]
[illegible] nach [illegible] gefahren ist. Ihr gehts ganz gut. Schon seit
längere Zeit ich erhalte keine Pakete und Briefe aus Zamość.
Ich bin sehr unruhig über Stef. Ich habe ein Paket [illegible]
erhalten, das machte mir grosse Freude. Ich bin ganz gesund
und erfreut mit Gedanken dass bald ich werde meine Kinder
in unter eigenen Dach begrüssen. Ich küsse Dich herzlich und
[illegible] Dich Gottesschütze. Hania K. Grüsst Dich herzlich.
Deine sehnende Mamusia.

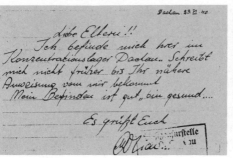

178

179

180

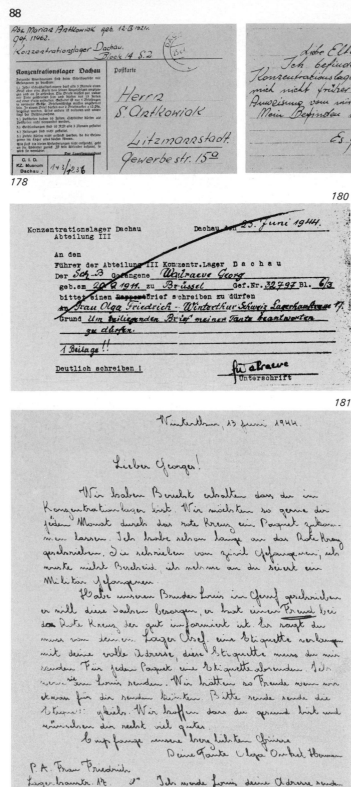

181

Concentration Camp Dachau
Department III   Dachau, June 23, 1944

To: The Chief of Department III, Dachau Concentration Camp
The Belgian protective custody prisoner Walraeve Georg, born:
Sep, 20, 1911, in Brussels, Prisoner number: 32797, Block 6/3,
requests that he may write a letter
To: Mrs. Olga Friedrich — Winterthur, Switzerland, Lagerhaus-
straße 17. Reason: To reply to the enclosed letter from my
aunt.

1 enclosure!   signature

Write clearly!

Wintherthur, June 13, 1944

Dear Georges,
We have been informed that you are in the concentration
camp. We would very much like to send you a parcel each
month through the Red Cross. I wrote to them quite some time
ago. In their reply they mentioned civilian prisoners but I did
not know, I presumed you were a military prisoner.
I have written to our brother Louis in Geneva, he will take care
of these things. He has got a friend in the Red Cross who is
very well informed. He says you should ask your camp commander for a label stating your full address. You should send
these labels to me; for each parcel one label. I will send them
to Louis. We would be so happy to be able to send you some-
thing. Please send the labels immediately. We hope that you
are in good health and wish you all the best.

    Warmest regards
    your aunt Olga and uncle Herman

PS. I will send Louis your address. Maybe a parcel can be sent
to this address the first time. It is safer if you send the labels in
case of change of address.

p.A. Mrs. Friedrich
Lagerhausstr. 17
Wintherthur
Switzerland

182
Dachau, 1938

183

Dachau Concentration Camp
Political Department   Nov. 18, 1933

P.P.

In answer to your post card we wish to inform you that the protective custody prisoner Otto Kaindl is in good health. He is unable to send you a message because the intrigues of a few communist scoundrels have made it necessary to impose a post ban. It is not known here when he will be released. Each case will be dealt with by the Bavarian Political Police in Munich.

Camp Commandant

First murder in the Dachau concentration camp

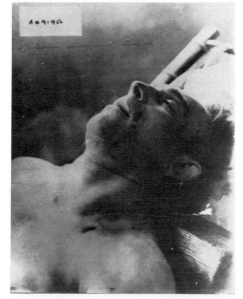

1933 — The Chief Public Prosecutor Wintersberger opens an inquiry on murder committed at Dachau

Sebastian Nefzger

Public Prosecutor's Office
Landgericht München II   Munich June 1, 1933

To the
Chief Public Prosecutor
Munich

Sub: Decease of protective custody prisoner Nefzger in Dachau concentration camp

On May 27, 1933 the Dachau County Court received the following information:
"Concentration Camp Dachau, Political Dept. to Dachau County Court May 27, 1933. The post mortem examination carried out on the prisoner Sebastian Nefzger, salesman, of 17, Schommerstr. Munich, born Jan 10, 1900 in Munich, Catholic, married, established that death was not due to any external influence. There exists no doubt that death was due to bleeding from a cut in the artery of the left wrist. signed: Dr. Nuernbergk, Camp Doctor."
Neither Dachau County Court nor the Public Prosecutor's Office, Munich II had at that point been informed of Nefzger's death although this occured during the night of May 25/26. The Dachau County Court informed the Public Prosecutor's Office, Munich II of this letter and a coroner's inquest was ordered, which took place on May 27, 1933. As the County Court doctor regarded death by bleeding to be doubtful, and because of a cord mark found on the neck of the corpse, the Public Prosecutor ordered an autopsy examination on May 29, 1933. The preliminary report states the following:
1) The results of the autopsy exclude bleeding from a cut on the left arm as cause of death,
II) The cut above the left wrist reveals three incisions in the bone. There are no attempted cuts. These findings contradict the assumption that the injuries were self-inflicted.
III) Asphyxia is presumed to have been the cause of death, probably caused by strangulation or suffocation. The position of the cord marks do not conform with those usually found in cases of hanging. 6 photographs were taken of the body before the autopsy took place, copies of which are enclosed.
Today I have filed a murder charge against unknown offenders, Commandant Wäckerle, the camp doctor Dr. Nuernbergk and a charge of complicity against senior secretary Mutzbauer. I have made an application for opening and execution of preliminary legal enquiries as well as a warrant of arrest for the aforementioned accused.
I will keep you informed as to the progress of the case.

The Chief Public Prosecutor

Az. G 886/33
Public Prosecutor's Office
Landgericht München II   Munich, June 1, 1933

To the Chief Public Prosecutor
Oberlandesgericht München

Re: Decease of protective custody prisoner Leonhard Hausmann in Dachau concentration camp

On May 17, 1933, the 31 year old married unskilled worker Leonhard Hausmann of Augsburg, a protective custody prisoner in Dachau concentration camp, was shot by SS Scharführer Karl Ehmann. According to Ehmann's account, Hausmann was detailed to dig up young fir trees in a forest area near the camp and carry them to a specified place. Ehmann was supervising him. Suddenly he lost sight of the prisoner and began to look for him. He saw him running away in a stooping posture. Ehman ran after him and ordered him to halt and to stay where he was, without success. Consequently Ehmann directed his pistol at the escapee without taking careful aim. He fired and Hausmann fell dead.

Ehman claims to have shot from a distance of between 10 to 12 metres. On May 17, 1933, a postmortem was carried out under the supervision of the county coroner which showed that death was due to a shot through the left thoracic cavity. According to this post-mortem report the shot was fired from a distance of less than 1 metre. In the meantime the institute for forensic medicine has established that the distance was less then 30 cm.

Today I have filed a charge against Ehmann together with an application for the opening and execution of preliminary legal enquiries I have also issued a warrant for his arrest as there is danger of his escaping or prejudicing the course of justice. I will keep you informed as to the progress of the case.

The Chief Public Prosecutor

Public Prosecutor's Office
Landgericht München II   Munich, June 2, 1933

To the
Ministry of Justice

Sub: Decease of protective custody prisoners in
Dachau Concentration Camp

Acting upon instructions I visited Police Commandant Himmler in his office in the Munich Police Headquarters at midday on June 1, 1933. We discussed at great length incidents which had occured in Dachau concentration camp, a detailed report of which I had already sent to the Ministry of Justice for the state. We specifically discussed the cases of Schloß, Hausmann, Strauss and Nefzger, about which he appeared to be already informed. I showed him photographs taken from the investigation files. I pointed out that preliminary findings had substantiated the strong suspicion that individual members of the camp guards and camp officials were guilty of criminal offences. I went on to say that the Public Prosecutor and the Police authorities had been informed of these cases and were obliged to prefer charges, regardless of the persons involved. I asked Police Commandant Himmler for his utmost support in this matter.

I stated that I had applied for the opening of judicial inquiry proceedings in these four cases and that I would issue a warrant of arrest against the persons suspected of being criminally involved in these cases because of the danger of their prejudicing the course of justice. I further stated that I intended to seek the support of the responsible officers in the Munich Police Crime Department. Police Commandant Himmler approved of my application and ordered that I and the Investigation Officer should in no way be hindered in our inquiries in Dachau camp and that all requested information should be given. He declared that he had of course no objection to my other plans regarding the investigation of the individual cases.

Chief Public Prosecutor
Wintersberger

191   Wilhelm Franz

Sub: Death of protective custody prisoner Hugo Handschuch in Dachau concentration camp

Ref: report of September 19, 1933

According to the investigations which I have made so far, the suspicion that Handschuch had already been subjected to a considerable amount of bodily ill-treatment at the "Braunes Haus" in Munich on the day of his arrest on August 23, 1933 appears to be well founded. The suspicion that Handschuch did not die a natural death is further supported by the fact that the Political Police and the camp commandant explicitly refused to allow the relatives of the deceased to see the body. In order to ascertain the true cause of death I intend to make an application to the County Court in Dachau where the body lies buried in the local cemetery, for the exhumation of the body and coroner's post mortem examination. I shall inform you as to the results of this examination.

The Chief Public Prosecutor
Wintersberger

188

189

copy

No. G1848/33
Public Prosecutor's Office
Landgericht München II   Munich, Sept 26, 1933

To the
Ministry of Justice

Sub: Death of protective custody prisoner Hugo Handschuch in Dachau Concentration Camp

Re: My report of Sept 21, 1933

I ordered an official post-mortem which was carried out in Dachau on September 23, 1933. It showed that death was due to cerebral paralysis resulting from a haemorrhage in the soft brain cells caused by the application of a blunt instrument to the skull, especially to the area of the left temple and back of the head. In addition, extensive bleeding was found on the left cheek, the right shoulder, the left forearm, the buttocks, thighs and the left calf. This was caused by the application of a blunt instrument before death. The findings of the post-mortem and the preliminary medical evidence provide grounds for the suspicion that death was due to the fault of a third party.
I intend to continue the necessary investigation proceedings in cooperation with the political police.

Chief Public Prosecutor
Wintersberger

190

The Bavarian Minister of the Interior   Munich, November 29, 1933

To the Minister of Justice
Munich

Dear Fellow Party Member,
Minister Dr. Frank,

On Nov 18, 1933, the Commandant of the Political Police in the Ministry of the Interior submitted an application to you for the investigation proceedings in the case of the protective custody prisoners Hugo Handschuch, Wilhelm Franz and Delwin Katz to be quashed for reasons of State policy. You then sent the liaison officer of the Ministry of Justice to the Bavarian Political Police, Public Prosecutor Dr. Stepp, to my office.

In the meantime, in a consultation with the Chief of the Political Police Reichsführer SS Himmler, it was once again confirmed that the continuation of these investigation proceedings would be detrimental to the image of the National Socialist State as the proceedings are directed against members of the SS and SA and therefore against the whole of the SS and SA who are the main supporters of the National Socialist State. Because of these reasons I agree with the application of Nov 18, 1933, submitted by the Chief of the Political Police in the Ministry of the Interior, for the investigation proceedings be quashed.

The Chief of the Political Police Reichsführer SS Himmler informed me that you had a long discussion with him regarding this matter. It was also discussed in the Cabinet with the result that a delegate was sent by the Ministry of Justice to the Political Police. I trust that these are the last of such cases where the "Reichsstatthalter" and the Cabinet are compelled to intervene in order to protect State interests. I have made it clear to the Political Police Organization that in future in similar cases I am no longer prepared to quash investigation proceedings.

On the other hand I acknowledge the absolute necessity of providing the supervisors in concentration camps with adequate means to put down acts of aggression, subordination and serious offences against camp discipline, by immediate armed intervention, or court-martial executions.

copy

No. G 2138/33
Public Prosecutor's Office
Landgericht München II   Munich, Sept 27, 1934

To the
Chief Public Prosecutor
Munich

Sub: Decease of protective custody prisoners Wilhelm Franz
      and Dr. Katz in Dachau Concentration Camp

I have dismissed the case as the inquiry did not produce sufficient evidence to prove that the death of the two protective custody prisoners was due to the fault of a third party.

                          The Chief Public Prosecutor
                          Dr. Barnickel

193

195

199

198

210

211

212

213

Antijüdische Aktionen in Berlin und dem Reich

dnb. Berlin, 10. 11.

Nach Bekanntwerden des Ablebens des durch feige jüdische Mörderhand niedergestreckten deutschen Diplomaten Pg. vom Rath haben sich im ganzen Reich spontane judenfeindliche Kundgebungen entwickelt.

Die tiefe Empörung des deutschen Volkes machte sich dabei auch vielfach in starken antijüdischen Aktionen Luft.

Wie in allen Teilen des Reiches haben sich auch in Berlin scharfe judenfeindliche Kundgebungen ereignet. An vielen Stellen hat man die Schaufensterscheiben der jüdischen Geschäfte eingeschlagen und die Schaukästen der jüdischen Ladenbesitzer demoliert. Die Waren selbst sind unberührt geblieben. Die jüdischen Geschäftsinhaber besaßen noch die Frechheit, durch ihre arischen Angestellten die Glasscherben mit den Fingern beseitigen zu lassen, was den leidenschaftlichen Protest der Passanten hervorrief.

In den Synagogen, den Stätten, an denen die staats- und volksfeindlichen Lehren des Talmud und des Schulchan-Aruch verbreitet werden, wurde Feuer angelegt, das die Inneneinrichtung zerstörte. Da die Volksgenossen äußerste Disziplin bewahrten, ist keinem Juden auch nur ein Haar gekrümmt worden.

Aehnliche Vorgänge spielten sich auch in den Berliner Vororten und in märkischen Ortschaften ab. So wird aus Potsdam gemeldet, daß sich nach dem Bekanntwerden der Nachricht vom Tod des Gesandtschaftsrats vom Rath der Bevölkerung eine ungeheure Erregung bemächtigte, die sich in Angriffen auf jüdische Läden und in der Zerstörung der Schaufenster auswirkte. Die Synagoge am Wilhelmsplatz wurde ebenfalls in Mitleidenschaft gezogen. Hier sollen Waffen gefunden worden sein.

In Eberswalde ist die Synagoge in Flammen aufgegangen, das gleiche Schicksal wurde den jüdischen Tempeln in Cottbus und in Brandenburg bereitet.

*

Berlin, 10. 11.

In der Synagoge in Berlin-Wilmersdorf, Prinzregentenstraße, brach heute morgen zwischen 6 und 7 Uhr ein Brand aus. Die Kuppel ist bereits eingestürzt.

*

or. Nürnberg, 10. 11. (Eigenbericht)
Unter dem Eindruck der Pariser Nachricht vom Tode des Gesandtschaftsrates vom Rath bildeten sich heute morgen in Nürnberg Demonstrationszüge, die ihrer Empörung über die gemeine Tat des Juden Grünspan Luft machten. Die Empörung richtete sich gegen die noch in Nürnberg bestehenden jüdischen Geschäfte, die demoliert wurden.

*

kl. Essen, 10. 11. (Eigenbericht)
Im Laufe der vergangenen Nacht und in den Morgenstunden kam es in den Städten des Ruhrreviers und am Niederrhein zu Kundgebungen gegen die Juden. Der Zorn empörter Menschen richtete sich gegen die jüdischen Ladengeschäfte, die zerstört wurden. In Essen, Düsseldorf und Krefeld und anderen Orten brennen zur Stunde die Synagogen. In Essen ist auch das eben fertiggestellte große jüdische Jugendhaus, das eine Zentralstelle der jüdischen Jugendverbände war, in Flammen aufgegangen.

*

lg. Leipzig, 10. 11. (Eigenbericht)
In Leipzig ist es in der vergangenen Nacht zu spontanen Kundgebungen gegen das Judentum gekommen. Gegen Morgen brach im Konfektionshaus Bamberger & Hertz am Augustusplatz und in der Synagoge in der Gottschedstraße Feuer aus. Der Feuerwehr gelang es, die umstehenden Gebäude vor dem Uebergreifen des Brandes zu bewahren. In sämtlichen jüdischen Detailgeschäften wurden die Fensterscheiben zerschlagen.

20 Jahre Schutzhaft für Juden, die Waffen besitzen

Eine Anordnung des Reichsführers SS Himmler

dnb. München, 10. 11.

Der Reichsführer SS und Chef der deutschen Polizei, hat folgende Anordnung erlassen:

Personen, die nach den Nürnberger Gesetzen als Juden gelten, ist jeglicher Waffenbesitz verboten. Zuwiderhandelnde werden in Konzentrationslager übergeführt und auf die Dauer von 20 Jahren in Schutzhaft genommen.

Berlin, Nov 10,

The announcement of the decease of the diplomat and party member vom Rath by the cowardly hand of the Jewish murderer has aroused spontaneous anti-Jewish demonstrations throughout the Reich. The German Peoples' profound indignation has given vent to powerful anti-Jewish activities.

In Berlin as in other parts of the Reich, drastic anti-Jewish demonstrations have taken place. In many places Jewish shop windows have been smashed and the show-cases of Jewish shopkeepers wrecked. The goods themselves remained untouched. Passers-by protested violently as Jewish shop owners had the audacity to instruct their Arian employees to remove the pieces of broken glass with their fingers.

The synagogues from which the teachings of the Talmud and the Schulchan Aruch are spread, teachings hostile to the State and People, have been set on fire and the furnishings destroyed. Thanks to the discipline of the "Volksgenossen" not one finger was laid on the Jews themselves.

Similar incidents also occured in other outlying districts of Berlin and in the surrounding provinces. It is reported from Potsdam that the announcement of diplomat vom Rath's death caused great indignation among the population and resulted in attacks on Jewish shops and the destruction of window-displays. The synagogue in Wilhelmsplatz was also affected — arms are said to have been found there.

The synagogue in Eberwalde went up in flames and the Jewish temples in Cottbus and Brandenburg suffered the same fate.

Berlin — Nov 10

Fire broke out between 6 and 7 this morning in the Berlin Wilmersdorf synagogue in Prinzregenten-street. The dome has already collapsed.
(Similar reports from Nuremberg, Leipzig, Essen.)

20 YEARS PROTECTIVE CUSTODY FOR JEWS FOUND IN POSSESSION OF ARMS!

Munich Nov 10,

A decree from SS Reichsführer Himmler The Reichsführer and Chief of the German Police issued the following decree:

No one classified under the Nuremberg laws as a Jew is allowed to possess firearms of any description. Those who disregard this law will be sent to a concentration camp and taken into protective custody for a term of 20 years.

Judenbann=Bezirke in Berlin

Vom 6. Dezember an zunächst Straßen im Regierungsviertel gesperrt
Wohnungsaufgabe im Westen angeraten

215

DISTRICTS IN BERLIN BARRED TO JEWS

From 6 December the first streets in the government quarter will be barred to Jews. LEAVING OF FLATS IN WEST END ADVISED.

The Chief of Police issues to the Berlin Police District the following first directive in conjunction with the Reichs Police regulation of Nov 28, 1938, regarding the appearance of Jews in public. It is to take effect from Dec 6, 1938.

FIRST DIRECTIVE TO THE REICHS POLICE ORDER OF Dec 5, 1938, REGARDING APPEARANCE OF JEWS IN PUBLIC.

In accordance with the Police decree of Nov 28, 1938, the following instructions are to be observed with regard to Jews in public.

In accordance with the Police decree of Nov 28, 1938, the following instructions are to be observed with regard to Jews in public.

§ 1

No Jew, either of German nationality or stateless, may set foot in or drive through the streets, squares, parks or buildings which have been barred to Jews.

§ 2

All Jews, both German and stateless, who at the time thisdecree takes effect, still live in this restricted area are required to obtain a permit from their local police station in order to pass through the area. These permits will not be distributed to occupants after July 1, 1939.

§ 3

Jews both German and stateless, who are required to report inside the restricted area must obtain a 12 hour permit from their local police station.

§ 4

In Berlin Jews are barred from the following places:

1. All theatres, cinemas, cabarets, publik concert halls and auditoriums, museums, amusement parks, the exhibition halls in the Messedamm (exhibition street) including the exhibition grounds and the radio tower, the Deutschland Halle, the Sport Palast, the Reichs Sport ground, all sports grounds including the skating rink.

2. All public and private swimming pools, including outdoor pools.

3. Wilhelmstrasse from Leipzigerstrasse to Unter den Linden including Wilhelmsplatz.

4. etc

5. etc

216

ONLY JEWISH FIRST NAMES FOR JEWS

Application of the law regarding surnames and first names. A private telegramme from the "Frankfurter Zeitung".

Berlin 23 August. The Minister of the Interior and the Minister for Justice have issued a second decree with regard to the application of the law for changes in surnames and first names. Accordingly, Jews of German nationality and stateless Jews may only adopt those first names specified by the Minister of the Interior in his directives for first names. This does not apply to Jews of foreign nationalities. In so far as Jews have other first names than those specified in the above mentioned decree, they must take on an additional name from 1 January. Males must adopt the name Israel, females Sarah.

220

IF YOU SEE THIS SIGN... JEW

You must ensure by your behaviour towards Jews that Judaism will never again achieve the slightest influence in our nation. Recognize the true enemy!

The "Reichskristallnacht", the anti-Jewish pogrom throughout Germany in November 1938

218

219

217 For Aryans only

221

222

223

224

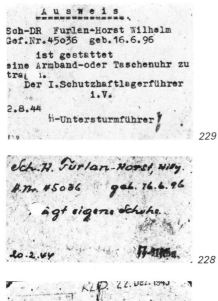

225 List of prisoners' personal effects *226*

Special permits, allowing prisoners in exceptional cases to wear a watch, their own shoes or have a normal hair style (instead of having their heads shaved).

229

228

227

✓	1	Walraeve Georg	
✓	2	Demaret Moritz	
✓	3	Mallot Jacques	
✓	4	Lauries Arlin	
✓	5	Gonzales Mariano	
✓	6	Lopez Vargas Fernando	
✓	7	Sledzinski Stefan	
✓	8	Marlier Charles	
✓	9	Auboiroux Germain	
	10	Michelet Edmond	
✓	11	Mosenko Tichon	
✓	12	Kaminski Wenzel	

230

Fragebogen für Häftlinge

1. a) Name und Vorname des Gefangenen
   b) Gefangenenbezeichnung
   c) Häftlingsnummer
   d) Zugegangen in Block — Stube
   e) Zugang am
   f) überstellt
   g) rücküberstellt
   h) überstellt
   i) rücküberstellt
   k) entlassen

2. Beruf

3. Geboren am .... und Ort
3a. Letzter Wohnort und Adresse

4. Religion¹)

5. Wieviel Kinder?²) In welchem Alter? Beruf der Kinder

5a. Verheiratet? Mit wem?

6. a) Größe
   b) Gewicht³) (ev. lezt. vor d. Verhaftg.)
   c) Farbe der Haare
   d) Farbe der Augen
   e) Kopfform

7. Sind Tätowierungen vorhanden? An welchen Körperstellen?

8. Leben Vater und Mutter noch? Deren Alter? Im Todesfalle: In welchem Alter gest.? Woran?

¹) In der Gef. nach einer Religionsgemeinschaft angehörten, so ist dies unter Angabe des Zeitpunktes zu vermerken.
²) ...
³) ...

9. Sind bei Vater und Mutter körperliche oder geistige Leiden vorgekommen? (Tuberkulose, Nervenkrankheiten — Aufenthalt in einer (welcher?) Nerven-Heilanstalt, Krämpfe, Blindheit, Taubheit, körperliche Mißbildungen, Alkoholismus — Aufenthalt in einer Trinkerheilanstalt (welcher?))

10. Sind in der Familie⁴) die in Ziff. 9 bezeichneten Krankheiten oder Zustände vorgekommen? (Bei wem?) genaue Anschrift des Erkrankten — in Todesfalle letzte Anschrift des Verstorbenen —, Bezeichnung des Verwandtschaftsverhältnisses zum G. (Beispiel: Bruder der Mutter, Straßenbahnschaffner Alois Meier, verst. 1932 an Gehirnschlag, litt an Krämpfen, war 1930 in der Nerven-Heilanstalt in X., zuletzt wohnhaft in München, Dachauer Straße 1)

11. Sind in der Familie⁴) des G. Selbstmordversuche vorgekommen? (Bei wem?) Sind verbrecherische oder asoziale Veranlagungen beobachtet? (Bei wem?) (Sittlichkeits-, Eigentums- und Gewalttätigkeits-Vergehen, Bettelei und Landstreicherei, Vergehen unter Einfluß des Alkohols?)

12. An welchen Krankheiten hat der G. selbst gelitten? Wann und wo (insbes. Krankenhaus, Arzt) ist er behandelt? Sind Unfälle (Kopfverletzungen), Vergiftungen (Gasvergiftungen oder Verschüttungen im Felde) vorgekommen? War der G. geschlechtskrank? Wo, wann und von wem behandelt?

⁴) Zur Familie des Gef. gehören die Eltern, deren Eltern (Großeltern), sowie deren Abkömmlinge, also auch die Geschwister, sowie Geschwisterkinder und Kinder des Gef. Der Gef. ist besonders darauf zu achten, ob bestimmte Krankheiten z. B. Tuberkulose, Nerven- und Geisteskrankheiten, Blindheit, Taubheit, Mißbildung ...

13. Welche Schulen, wo und wann hat der G. besucht? Wie waren die Leistungen? (gut, normal, mangelhaft) Ist der G. sitzen geblieben? Wie oft?

14. Hat der G. eine Schule, Anstalt für Minderbegabte (Wo und welche Anstalt? Wann?) besucht?

15. Ist bezüglich des G. Fürsorgeerziehung angeordnet? (Wann? Grund?) In welcher Anstalt bzw. Familie war der G. untergebracht?

16. Ist der G. vorbestraft?²) Wann? Wegen welcher Tat? Von welchem Gericht? Ist eine strafbare Handlung unter dem Einfluß von Alkohol begangen?

17. Hat der G. Rauschgifte gebraucht? Welche? Ist eine Entziehungskur angeordnet? Wann? Mit welchem Erfolg?

18. Ist der G. a) Nichtraucher
    b) Nichttrinker
    Seit wann?
    Wär er es früher? Bis wann?

²) Unter Vorstrafen sind auch Geldstrafen zu verstehen, soweit sie nicht Polizeiübertretungen betreffen. Desgl. ist auch solche Strafen aufzuführen, deren Verbüßung ganz oder teilweise durch Amnestie erlassen ist.

231

Questionnaire – prisoners' personal data and medical history

232

233

234

Certificate of discharge: Max Hohenberg

236

Kanzlei des Führers
Party Political Office
To the Foreign Office
Berlin W. 8
Wilhelmstr. 74/76
SECRET!

Berlin W. 9
August 19, 1937

Sub: Dr. Kurt Schumacher at present in protective custody.

In her application of 10 May, 1937, Miss Maria Fiechtl of Chicago III., 4402 N. Ashland Ave., U.S.A., makes a request to the Führer for the release of her fiancé from Dachau Concentration Camp.

A one-time Social Democrat M.P., "Reichsbannerführer" and editor of the "Schwäbische Tageswacht", Dr Schumacher cannot be released from the camp as his radical Marxist attitudes present a direct danger to public safety. It is to be expected that upon release he would immediately emigrate and then agitate against Germany from abroad. This is all the more to be expected as several like-minded friends of his, who are in a position to give him financial support, are already promoting anti-German propaganda. For these reasons he cannot yet be released.

I request that Fiechtl be informed in the appropriate manner that her fiancé Dr. Schumacher cannot yet be released, without mentioning the above reasons.

Heil Hitler!

File card: Charles Delestraint

237

List of prominent prisoners to be
transferred from Dachau to Innsbruck

238

235

Berlin, Oct 20, 1937

re: letter of Oct 19,—II c—
sub: Dr. Schumacher, at present in protective custody

According to information from the German Consulate General in Chicago dated 28 inst. Miss Maria Fichtl was instructed to appear at the consulate where she was informed of the rejection of her application without any further explanation.

signed:
Kanzlei des Führers der NSDAP
Parteipolitisches Amt
Hermann Göringstr. 15

239

240

Work with the road-roller, 1933

246

Owing to the temporary evacuation of the Dachau camp, prisoners worked in the stone-quarries of Mauthausen und Flossenbürg

248

249

The Communal Housing and Homesteads Company Ltd. Dachau

Berlin, January 10, 1939

The following members of the board of directors pass the following resolution:

1. The costs incurred in the first three construction stages do not include those of removing the earth which was carried out by prisoners from Dachau concentration camp and not by private firms. In order to calculate the total cost of the housing project it is necessary to credit the cost of the earth removal work done by the prisoners in the company's account ledgers.

2. According to the enclosed estimate by architect Dinkel of December 17, 1938, the value of the work carried out by prisoners is 65 351 RM. This estimate contains several calculation errors. The architect's calculation was inaccurate to an amount of almost 3000 RM.

To cover the prison labour costs involved in removing the earth in the first three construction stages, it has been decided that the sum of 70 000 RM be credited to the company's account and that the society for the promotion and fostering of German cultural memorials, the financers of this project, be credited ...

copy to:	signed:
SS-Gruppenführer Pohl	SS-Gruppenführer ...
SS-Standartenführer Nöckel	SS-Standartenführer ...
SS-Obersturmbannführer	
Dr. Salpeter	SS-Untersturmbannführer

250

Stab W   Berlin Oct, 18, 1944
To the Chief W
via SS-Hauptsturmführer Dr. Hoffmann

Sub: Increased productivity

Re: Discussion with party member Boldt from a suboffice of the German work front, dated Oct 14, 1944

The Reichsführer SS is of the opinion that the task of the guard detachments is not only to supervise the protective custody prisoners and the prisoners of war but also to force an increase in work tempo and productivity. Party member Boldt intends to provide me with a copy of this communication from the Reichsführer SS.

signed:
SS-Obersturmführer

251

252

Dachau 1938

Concentration camp prisoners work for the armaments industry

List of armament factories working for the German Air Force specifying number of prisoners, working hours per month and articles

Lager und Betrieb	Anzahl der vorgesehen	Häftlinge eingesetzt	gel. Arb. Stunden im Monat Januar	Arbeitsleistung
Auschwitz:				Bau von Flakstellungen
Flakausbaustab, Auschw.	250	191	48 788	
Ost-Maschinenbau GmbH				Flakgeschützfertigung
Schwientochlowitz	1 500	730	196 067	Prod. Ergebnis Januar: 105 Geschütze
Siemens u. Schuckert, Auschwitz	1 500	90	19 240	zunächst Ausbau der Fertigungswerkstätten, später Schalt- u. Steuergeräte für Nachtjäger
Buchenwald:				
Erla-Maschinenwerk GmbH, Leipzig	2 800	1 550	176 105	Flugzeugteilefertigung Prod. Ergebnis Januar: 360 Flugzeugtragflächen BF 109, 290 Rümpfe BF 109, 304 Leitwerkträger
Junkers-Flug- u. Motorenwerke AG, Schönebeck	2 000	1 310	362 619	Flugzeugteilefertigung
Polte, Arnstadt	100	87	24 112	Aufbereitung von Flakpatronenhülsen Prod. Ergebnis Januar: 181 000 Flakpatronenhülsen
Leichtmetallwerke Rautenbach, Wernigerode	1 200	772	189 832	Fertigung von Zylinderblocks für Flugzeugmotore
Dachau:				
Rev. F. Hochfrequenzforschung	15	15	3 290	Hochfrequenzentwicklungsarbeiten
BMW, München-Allach	12 000	3 434	908 606	Flugzeugmotorenfertigung / Baumaßnahmen u. Stollenbau
Dornier-Werke GmbH Neuaubing	3 000	60	9 527	zunächst Aufbau des Arbeitslagers, später Flugzeugteilefertigung
Dr. Ing. Kimmel, München	25	23	7 925	Fertigung von Funkmeßgeräten Prod. Ergebnis Januar: 35 R C Generatoren
Luftfahrtforschungsanstalt, München	400	40	– –	Errichtung der Luftfahrtforschungsanstalt Ottobrunn
Messerschmitt AG, Augsburg/Haunstetten	3 400	2 695	740 640	Flugzeugferigung Me
Messerschmitt AG, Gablingen	600	352		Flugzeugfertigung Me
Messerschmitt AG, Dachau	600	192	35 766	Fertigung von Flugzeugeinzelteilen
Messerschmitt AG, Kottern	1 000	341	57 050	zunächst Ausbau der Fertigungswerkstätten, später Flugzeugteilefertigung.
Planungsstelle der Luftwaffe, Sudelfeld	25	25	4 660	Bau einer Versuchsanlage des Bev. für Hochfrequenz
Präzifix, Dachau	400	356	94 067	Anfertigung von Flugzeugnormteilen u. -schrauben
U. Sachse KG, Kempten	1 000	374	91 630	zunächst Ausbau der Fertigungswerkstätten / Beginn der Fertigung von Luftschraubenverstellgeräten.
Flossenbürg:				
Dt. Erd- u. Steinwerke GmbH, Flossenbürg	4 000	1 911	422 158	Flugzeugteilefertigung f. Messerschmitt Prod. Ergebnis Januar: 900 Satz Nasenkasten u. Kühlerverkleidungen 120 000 Einzelteile
Erla-Maschinenwerk GmbH, Johanngeorgenstadt	600	546	117 524	Flugzeugteilefertigung
Erla-Mülsen	500	30	– –	Flugzeugteilefertigung
Keramische Werke Bohemia, Neurohlau	100	100	10 764	Flugzeugteilefertigung f. Messerschmitt
Luftfahrtgerätewerk. Zwodau	1 500	199	28 314	Gerätefertigung f. d. Luftwaffe
Herzogenbusch:				
Dt.-Erd- u. Steinwerke GmbH, Herzogenbusch	600	411	35 248	Flugzeugzerlegbetrieb Prod. Ergebnis Januar: 12 Flugzeuge zerlegt, 35 Motore demontiert, 120 Tragflächen zerlegt
Feldbauamt 3 d. Luftwaffe	1 000	265	64 800	Rollstraßenbau für Flugplatz
Mauthausen:				
Dt. Erd-u. Steinwerke GmbH, Mauthausen	500	423	82 632	Flugzeugteilefertigung f. Messerschmitt Prod. Ergebnis Januar: 25 Flugzeugrümpfe
Flugmotoren GmbH Wiener-Neudorf	3 000	1 983	417 328	zunächst Baumaßnahmen, später Flugmotorenteilefertigung
Heinkel-Werke AG, Schwechat	3 200	2 065	486 206	Flugzeugteilefertigung

produced

Lager und Betrieb	Anzahl der vorgesehen	Häftlinge eingesetzt	gel. Arb. Stunden im Monat Januar	Arbeitsleistung
Natzweiler:				
Dt.-Erd-u. Steinwerke GmbH, Natzweiler	400	261	63 221	Demontage v. Ju-Motoren u. Schweißen v. Lufttorpedos
Neuengamme:				
*) stram, Hamburg-Bergedorf	80	80	21 554	Flugzeugteilefertigung
Messap GmbH, Hamburg-Langenhorn	120	110	31 422	Fertigung von Zünderlaufwerken
				Prod. Ergebnis Januar: 16 800 Unruhen S 30, 53 900 Unruhen S 60, 15 600 Zeitzünder S 30, 46 700 Zeitzünder S 60
Ravensbruck:				
Erprobungsstelle der RLM, Peenemünde-W.	600	598	125 000	
Gerätewerk Pommern GmbH Stargard	550	283	81 129	Baumaßnahmen
Heinkel Werke AG, Barth	2 000	1 721	435 155	Herstellung von Lufttorpedos
Mechan. Werkstätten GmbH Neubrandenburg	4 000	1 981	529 126	Flugzeugfertigung Fertigung von Bombenabwurfgeräten u. Fz. G 76
				Prod. Ergebnis Januar: 23 000 Schloss 50/X, 1 500 Schloss 2000, 150 PVC 1006, 500 Rudermaschinen, 400 ER 4 L-,,2''
Siemens u. Halske, Berlin Werk Ravensbrück	2 400	872	242 867	**Fertigung von Nachrichtengeräten (u.a. Kehlkopfmikrofone)**
Silva-Metallwerke GmbH, Genthin	600	596	154 224	Herstellung von Flakmunition Prod. Ergebnis Januar: 518 200 2 cm Patronen, 927 500 2 cm Patronen (div. Ausf.), 965 000 13 mm Patronen
Veltener-Maschinenbau GmbH, Velten	600	596	146 873	Herstellung von Flugzeugeinzelteilen
Sachsenhausen:				
Heinkel-Werke AG, Oranienburg	6 500	5 939	1 699 978	Flugzeugserienbau Prod. Ergebnis Januar: 15 Flugzeugzellen He 177
Luftschiffbau Zeppelin GmbH, Oranienburg	300	221	54 006	Herstellung u. Instandsetzung von Ballon Prod. Ergebnis Januar: 120 Ballons instandgesetzt u. Teilarbeiten f. 40 neue Ballons
Ostland-KL:				
Feldbauleitung d. Luftwaffe, Spilve	1 000	1 000	280 776	Herrichtung des Flugplatzes
Feldbauleitung 3/I, Kauen	1 000	829	222 186	Ausbau des Flughafens
Flakbeuteinstandsetzungswerkstatt, Kauen	200	162	4 920	Umarbeitung erbeuteter Flak
Kopperschmidt u. Söhne, Riga	20	20	6 160	Herstellung v. Flugzeugkampfständen
Als weitere Einsätze wurden in diesen Tagen vereinbart:				
Buchenwald:				
Anhydrit	10 000	— —	— —	Fertigung für Junkers in Stollen
Ago, Oschersleben	1 500	— —	— —	Flugzeugfertigung Focke-Wulf-Jäger
Groß-Rosen:				
Famo, Bunzlau	1 500	— —	— —	Montagebetrieb für FW-Nachtjäger Ta 154
Mauthausen:				
Esche II	10 000	— —	— —	Art der Fertigung wird durch RLM noch entschieden
Natzweiler:				
Gerätewerk Pommern GmbH Werk Diedenhofen	600	— —	— —	Herstellung von Lufttorpedos
	90 785	35 839	8 733 495	

Der Chef des SS-Wirtschafts-Verwaltungshauptamtes
Pohl

SS-Obergruppenführer und General der Waffen-SS

Berlin, den 21. Februar 1944

Food Rations

In theory:

Weekly Rations:				
period of Time:	Aug 1, 1940 to May 14, 1942	May 15, 1943 to April 27, 1944	April 28, 1944 to Feb 28, 1945	from March 1, 1945
Meat or meat products: .	400 gr	280 gr	200 gr	250 gr
Fat	200 gr	170 gr	182,5 gr	83,33 gr
of which Margarine, Suet etc.	50 gr	40 gr		
Curds	100 gr	100 gr	100 gr	41,66 gr
or cheese from Skimmed milk	50 gr	50 gr		
Bread	2740 gr	2450 gr	2600 gr	1750 gr
Sugar	80 gr	80 gr	80 gr	—
Jam	100 gr	100 gr	100 gr	250 gr
Cereals	150 gr	150 gr	255 gr	—
Flour or flour mixture . . .	225 gr	125 gr	125 gr	—
Skimmed milk	—	—	0,25 l daily	0,25 l daily
Coffee substitute	84 gr	63 gr	62,5 gr	33,33 gr
Potatoes	3500 gr	5000 gr	2800 gr	3500 gr
Fresh vegetables root crops etc.	2800 gr	2600 gr	4000 gr	375 gr

Supplement for prisoners engaged in heavy work				
Period of time:	Aug 1, 1940 to May 14, 1942	May 15, 1942 to April 27, 1944	April 28, 1944 to Feb 28, 1945	from March 1, 1945:
Meat or meat products	400 gr	280 gr	280 gr	350 gr
Fat	100 gr	100 gr	100 gr	56,66 gr
Bread	1400 gr	1400 gr	1400 gr	1100 gr

In practice:

Morning:	350 gr ration of bread for the whole day 1/2 l substitute coffee
Midday:	6 times per week: 1 lt. turnip or cabbage soup once a week: 1 lt. noodle soup
Evening:	4 times per week: 20–30 gr sausage or cheese 3/4 lt. substitute tea 3 times per week: 1 lt. soup

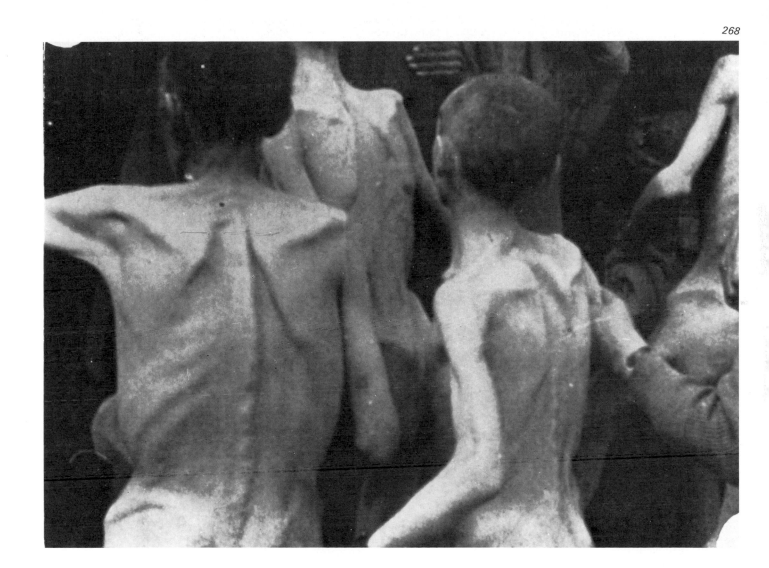

Transports to Dachau and from Dachau to other camps

(taken from the camp office files)

	prisoner transports to Dachau		prisoner transports from Dachau to other camps	
August 1944	from Auschwitz	1 601	to Auschwitz	129
	from Buchenwald	40	to Bergen-Belsen	15
	from Flossenbürg	1	to Buchenwald	228
	from Kowno	1 800	to Flossenbürg	1 403
	from Natzweiler	20	to Gross-Rosen	2
	from Neuengamme	10	to Mauthausen	1 735
	from Ravensbrück	38	to Natzweiler	564
	from Stutthof	550	to Ravensbrück	1
	from Warschau	3 954		
September 1944	from Auschwitz	2 504	to Flossenbürg	337
	from Auschwitz/ Stutthof	3 450	to Mauthausen	2 100
	from Gross-Rosen	33	to Natzweiler	2 318
	from Mauthausen	17	to Ravensbrück	63
	from Natzweiler	7 184	to Stutthof	10
	from Ravensbrück	500		
	from Sachsenhausen	25		
	from Stutthof	50		

269

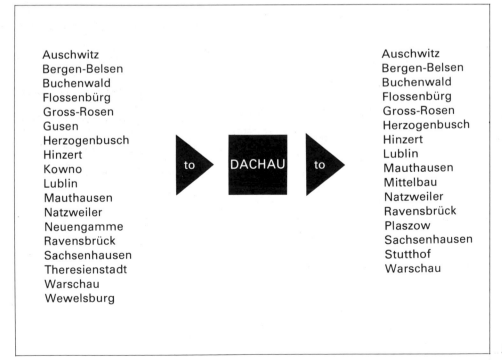

Auschwitz
Bergen-Belsen
Buchenwald
Flossenbürg
Gross-Rosen
Gusen
Herzogenbusch
Hinzert
Kowno
Lublin
Mauthausen
Natzweiler
Neuengamme
Ravensbrück
Sachsenhausen
Theresienstadt
Warschau
Wewelsburg

to DACHAU to

Auschwitz
Bergen-Belsen
Buchenwald
Flossenbürg
Gross-Rosen
Herzogenbusch
Hinzert
Lublin
Mauthausen
Mittelbau
Natzweiler
Ravensbrück
Plaszow
Sachsenhausen
Stutthof
Warschau

270

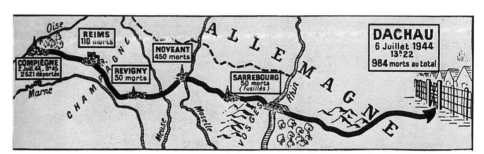

271

Departure Compiègne:
July 2, 1944 −2,521 deportees

Arrival Dachau:
July 6, 1944 −984 dead

272

Laon, June 19, 1944

I was at Venizel (Aisne) railway station yesterday as a train load of deportees for Germany passed through. I was given several addresses of which one was yours, presumably written by your son. I shall detach the part of the list which is of interest to you and hope that it is your son's handwriting. At the end of the list they state that they have come from Compiègne (Oise) camp on June 18, and are being deported to Germany. Their morale is good. Unfortunately that is all that I can tell you.

Dienststelle: **SS-Standort-Funkstelle Auschwitz**   Stelle: _____   (102)

Spruch-Nr.	Befördert am 30. Okt. 193 11	Uhr durch
	Aufgenommen am 193	Uhr durch
	Erhalten am 193	Uhr

Z Spruch Nr. 152 von

Vermerke:

Absendende Stelle:

te Meldung	Ort	Tag Monat	Stunde Minute
Abgegangen			
Angekommen			

Un **W.V.- Hauptamt
Amt D II
Oranienburg.**

30.10.42

Die 499 aus Dachau überstellten Häftlinge sind
am 29.10.42 hier eingetroffen. Die Häftlinge
sind in denkbar schlechtester Verfassung, kör-
perlich sehr schwach - Muselmänner. Ein Drittel
vielleicht nach 14 tägiger Erholungszeit ein-
satzfähig. Für den Buna-Einsatz sind die Häftlinge vollkommen ausgeschlossen. Der Transport
teilt sich in 50 brauchbare und 162 ohne Beruf,
sowie in 287 Landarbeiter auf.
Am 30.10.42 sind 186 Häftlinge aus Ravensbrück
eingetroffen. Die körperliche Verfassung ist
besser als beim Dachauer Transport. Der Transport teilt sich in 128 brauchbare Berufe und in
58 ohne Berufe auf.

Erledigt

Funkstellenleiter

Abteilung III a

gez.Schwarz.

SS - Obersturmführer.

SS Radio Office
Auschwitz

Message No 152

To
Hauptamt—Amt D II
Oranienburg
Oct 30, 1942

The 499 transfer prisoners from Dachau arrived here on Oct 29, 1942. They were in the worst conceivable condition, and physically very weak "Muselmänner". A third of them may be fit for work after a two-week convalescent period. The prisoners were absolutely unsuitable for work on the "Buna" project. The group consists of 50 who are of use, 162 without a profession, and 287 agricultural workers. On Oct. 30, 1942 186 prisoners arrived from Ravensbrück — their physical condition is better than that of the Dachau prisoners. This group is made up of 128 with useful professions and 58 without a profession.

Dept. IIIa

signed: Schwarz
SS-Obersturmführer

274

Mauthausen

Profitability of Prisoners

279

SS-Wirtschaftsverwaltungshauptamt
Amtsgruppe D
—Concentration Camps—
D I/1 /Az: 14 f Allg/Ot/S
Geheim Tgb. Nr. 856/43

Oranienburg, July 15, 1943

Sub: Rationalization in registering of deaths

Ref: Letter D I/Az: 14 f Allg/Ot/S.— of June 25, 1943

Encl:—/

To the
Commandants of the Concentration Camps

Da. Sah. Bu. Mau. Flo. Neu. Au. Gr.Ro. Natz, Stu. Rav. Herz. Ri. Emb. War. und Auf. Lager Bergen-Belsen

An examination of the administrative proceedure employed in the registering of death cases in concentration camps has shown that in some camps a considerable number of unnecessary and out-dated forms are still in circulation of which 6 to 8 copies are distributed for filing in various departments.
So for instance all departments concerned are issued with a separate form registering the death of a prisoner.
In future one form is to be circulated to all departments concerned. The form is then to be added to the personal records as soon as the index card has been brought up to date.

280

To:
Mrs. . . . .

Dear Mrs. . . . .

Your husband reported sick on . . . .
and was subsequently admitted to the infirmary and placed under medical supervision. He received the best possible medical attention and care. In spite of all medical efforts it was not possible to cure the illness.
I offer you my condolence on this loss.
Your husband expressed the <u>following</u> _{no} last wishes:
I have directed the prisoners' property office of my camp to forward the deceased's estate to your address.

281

Text b:
(can be duplicated)

Concentration Camp . . . .,date

. . . .

To: . . . .
Mrs.: . . . .

. . . .

Your husband . . . ., born . . . .
died on . . . . as a result of (cause of death) . . . . in this hospital. The body was cremated on . . . . in the county crematorium.
The death certificate is enclosed.

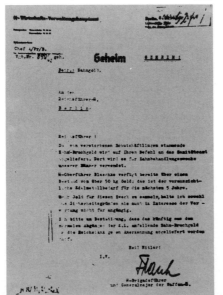

282

283

SS-Wirtschaftsverwaltungshauptamt   Oranienburg,
August 6, 1942

Amtsgruppe D – Concentration Camps
D II 288 Ma./Ha. Tgb. 112 geh.   SECRET!
Copy 13

Re: Use of hair cuttings

To the Commandants of the Concentration Camps
Arb., Au., Bu., Da., Flo., Gr.Ro., Lu., Maut/Gu., Na., Nie., Neu.,
Rav., Sahs., Stutth., Mor., SS SL Hinzert.

SS Obergruppenführer Pohl, Chief of the SS Wirtschafts-Ver-
waltungshauptamt has ordered that the hair of concentration
camp prisoners is to be put to use. Hair is to be made into industrial felt or spun into yarn. Women's hair is to be used in
the manufacture of hair-yarn-socks for 'U'-boat crews and
hair-felt foot-wear for the Reichs-railway.
It is therefore ordered that hair of female prisoners be desin-
fected and stored. Men's hair can only be put to use if it is
longer than 20 mm.
SS Obergruppenführer Pohl therefore agrees for an initial trial
period to the growing of the prisoners' hair to a length of
20 mm before it is cut. Long hair could facilitate escape and to
avoid this the camp commandants may have a middle parting
shaved in the prisoners' hair as a distinguishing mark, if they
think it necessary.
It is planned to set up a hair processing workshop in one of the
concentration camps. Further details as to the delivery of the
accumulated hair will follow.
The total monthly amount of male and female hair is to be reported to this office on the 5th of every month beginning from
September 5, 1942.

signed: Glücks
SS-Brigadeführer und
Generalmajor der Waffen-SS

SS-Wirtschaftsverwaltungshauptamt   Berlin,
October 8, 1942

Re: Gold fillings   SECRET!

To the Reichsführer SS
Berlin

Reichsführer!

In accordance with your order the gold from the teeth of dead
prisoners is to be delivered to the health department where it
will be used for the dental treatment of our men.
SS-Oberführer Blaschke already has 50 kilograms of gold at
his disposal which is expected to cover the requirements in
precious metal for the next 5 years.
In the interest of security and utilization of the gold, it is not
advisable to continue collection for this purpose.
I request confirmation that in future gold from dead prisoners
should be delivered to the Reichsbank upon acknowledge-
ment of receipt.

Heil Hitler!
Frank, SS-Brigadeführer und
Generalmajor der Waffen-SS

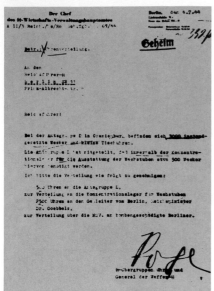

284

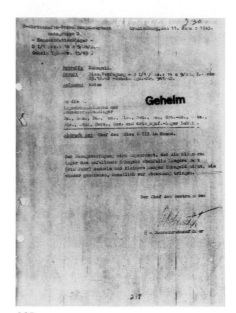

285

The Chief of the
SS-Wirtschaftsverwaltungshauptamt
A II/3 Reinh./Mo./Ro. Geh. Tgb. Nr. 61/44

Berlin, July 4, 1944
SECRET

Re: Distribution of clocks

To the Reichsführer SS
Berlin SW 11
Prinz Albrechtstr. 8

Reichsführer!

The Amtsgruppe D in Oranienburg has 3 000 repaired alarm clocks and other small table clocks.
The Amtsgruppe D has informed us that it requires approx. 500 of the alarm clocks for the concentration camp guard rooms. I request permission to distribute the clocks as follows: 500 clocks for the Amtsgruppe D, for concentration camp guard rooms. 2 500 clocks for the Berlin Gauleiter, Dr. Goebbels, for distribution through the NSV to Berlin citizens who have been bombed out.

signed: Pohl
SS-Obergruppenführer
General der Waffen-SS

SS- Wirtschaftsverwaltungshauptamt
Amtsgruppe D
D II/1 Az: 14 c 9/Ot/S
Geheim Tgb. Nr. 15 / 43   Oranienburg January 11, 1943

SECRET

sub: Gold fillings

ref: Our order – D I/1Az: 14 c 9/Ot J. of Dec 23, 1942 – Geheim Tgb. Nr. 941 / 42

Encl: none

To the Commandants of the Concentration Camps

Da. Sah. Bu. Flo. Neu. u. Gr. Ro. Natz. Nie. Stu. Herz. und Kriegsgef. Lager Lublin

In addition to the order referred to above, it is ordered that the smaller camps should also collect and keep the gold fillings for a longer period of time (one year) and not dispatch small amounts each month as has occured once again.

Chief of the Central Office
SS- Obersturmbannführer

287

286

SS-Wirtschaftsverwaltungshauptamt
Chief of Dept. D-Concentration Camps

Oranienburg, January, 19. 1943

Subject: Return of clothing belonging to prisoners
who died in concentration camps
Ref.: Order of July 11, 1942/DI/Az: 14 d 3 /Ot/U

Enclosures: none

SECRET

To the Commandants of the Concentration Camps
Da., Sah., Bu., Mau., Flo., Neu., Au., Gr.-Ro., Natz., Nie., Stu.,
Rav., KGL Lublin and Herzogenbusch

It was specifically stated in circular No.DI/Az.: 14 d 3/Ot./U of
July 11, 1942, that bloodstained clothing is not to be sent to relatives or distribution offices.
According to the Reichssicherheitshauptamt dirty and some-
times blood stained clothing has been sent to relatives in spite
of this specific order. I draw your attention once more to the
fact that utmost care is to be taken when handing over articles
of estate. All soiled clothing from dead prisoners is to undergo
a thorough cleaning before being dispatched, where cleaning
is not possible the articles are to be sent to the rag yard according to the order of the SS-Wirtschaftsverwaltungshauptamt
No. II/2a/420/12. 42/Ba/Scho/ of January 7, 1943.
The Camp Commandant is made personally responsible for
the execution of the above order.

signed: Liebehenschel
SS-Obersturmbannführer

Summary of costs for the upkeep of prisoners in concentration camp
The costs for clothing, accommodation and food per capita
and day are:
a) for female prisoners RM 1.22
b) for male prisoners RM 1.34

These sums were calculated as follows:

a) *Clothing*
The calculation of the costs of male clothing is based on the
supplies budget of January 18, 1944, (wear and tear) including cleaning and repair. The annual sum is:
RM 142.35 = per capita and day RM —.39
The calculation of the costs of female clothing is based on
the supplies budget of January 19, 1944, (wear and tear)
including cleaning and repair. The annual sum is:
RM 96.43 = per capita and day RM —.27

b) *Accommodation*
The cost of accommodation is based on H.Dv. 320/2 page
12, No. 56 and amounts per capita and day to: RM —.30
This includes:
a) camp equipment and replacement RM —.05
b) management costs (heating, lighting, cleaning, water
supply etc.) RM —.15
c) rent of premises RM —.10
total RM —.30

c) *Food*
According to the information supplied by the concentration
camp the cost of food, including supplements for prisoners
engaged in heavy work, per prisoner and day is RM —.65

Medical experiments in the camp infirmary

Der Reichsführer-SS
Persönlicher Stab

Tgb.-Nr. AR/704/24   Bra/V.

Bei Antwortschreiben bitte Tagebuch Nummer angeben.

Berlin SW 11, den   4.12.1941
Prinz-Albrecht-Straße 8
Führer-Hauptquartier

SS-Untersturmführer Dr. R a s c h e r
M ü n c h e n

Trogerstr.56

       Ihr Schreiben vom 24.11.1941 konnte ich dem
Reichsführer-SS vorlegen. Der Reichsführer-SS ist damit einverstanden,
daß die seinerzeit von ihm genehmigten Versuche an Konzentrations-
lagerhäftlingen im Lager Dachau ausgeführt werden. Die Inspektion
der K.L. ist angewiesen worden, den an den Versuchen beteiligten
Sanitätsoffizieren jeweils die Genehmigung zum Betreten des Lagers
zu gewähren.

                         H e i l   H i t l e r !

                         R. Brandt
                         SS-Sturmbannführer

Der Reichsführer SS
– Personal Staff –
Tgb. Nr. AR/704/24 Bra./V

Berlin SW 11, Dec 4, 1941
Prinz Albrechtstr. 8
Führer Headquarters

SS- Untersturmführer Dr. Rascher
München
Trogerstr. 56

I was able to present your letter dated Nov 24, 1941 to the Reichsführer SS. The Reichsführer SS has agreed to the conducting of the experiments already approved by him on prisoners in the Dachau camp. The concentration camp main office has been instructed to allow the medical officers concerned access to the camp.

Heil Hitler!
SS-Sturmbannführer

297

Dear Dr. Rascher,

Shortly before flying to Oslo, the Reichsführer SS gave me your letter of May 15, 1941, for partial reply. I can inform you that prisoners will of course be gladly made available for the high altitude experiments.

Dr. Sigmund Rascher   Munich,
Trogerstr. 56, 16 April, 1942

Most honourable Reichsführer,

Allow me to express my gratitude for your letter dated April 13, I was very pleased to learn of your great interest in these experiments and their results. I thank you for the suggestions which you made in your letter.

The experiment mentioned in the report dated 4. 4. has been repeated four times – always with the same results. The last subject Wagner, was revived through increased pressure after his respiration had stopped. Since the subject Wagner had been selected for a terminal experiment, a repetition of which did not promise any new results, and as your letter had not reached me, I subsequently initiated a new experiment which the subject did not survive.

Now I have one other request: May I photograph the individual organs which have been prepared in the Concentration Camp Pathology Department, in order to have a record of the unusual formations of the multiple air embolisms. My wife has already written to SS-Sturmbannführer Dr. Brandt with regard to this matter.

I remain your obedient servant,

Heil Hitler!
Your grateful servant
S. Rascher

298

Dr. Rascher to Camp Commandant Weiß, Dachau
Oct 10, 1942

The Russian prisoner of war Chonitsch . . . born May 24, 1920, was transferred to me on Sep 28, for experimental purposes. Chonitsch is a Russian who was to be executed. As the RF SS had ordered me to use persons sentenced to death for dangerous experiments, I wanted to conduct an experiment on this Russian which I was absolutely sure he would not survive. I reported at the time "You can be assured that the Russian will certainly not survive the experiment and will be dead by the given date." Contrary to all expectations the Russian in question survived 3 experiments which would have been fatal for any other person. In accordance with the RF SS' order that all test subjects who are sentenced to death but survive a dangerous experiment should be pardoned, I beg you to take the appropriate steps. I regret that the wrong assumption on our part has given rise to extra correspondence work.

With many thanks and Heil Hitler!

299

Reichssicherheitshauptamt
Teleprinter's Office

Oct, 20, 1942

Urgent
RF SS München Blitz Nr. 2020 20.10.42.1705
To: SS-Obersturmbannführer Dr. Brandt
Field Command Post (Feldkommandostelle) Hegewald
Highly esteemed Obersturmbannführer –
Will you please clarify the following case with the Reichsführer SS as soon as possible.
In the Reichsführer SS' letter of April 18, 1942 it is ordered in § 3 that if prisoners in Dachau condemned to death live through experiments which have endangered their lives, they should be pardoned. As up to now for these experiments only Poles and Russians were available, some of whom had been condemned to death, I am not certain whether the above mentioned § 3 is applicable to them or not and whether these persons after having survived repeated dangerous experiments may not be pardoned to life-long concentration camp imprisonment.
Request reply
by teleprint via Adjutancy RF-SS Munich

300

Teleprint

To
SS-Obersturmführer Schnitzler
München

Please inform SS-Untersturmführer Dr. Rascher with regard to his teleprint inquiry that the instruction given some time ago by the Reichsführer SS concerning the pardoning of experimental subjects does not apply to Poles and Russians.

signed: Brandt
SS-Obersturmbannführer

Oct 21, 1942
Bra./Dr.

301 *302* *303* *304*

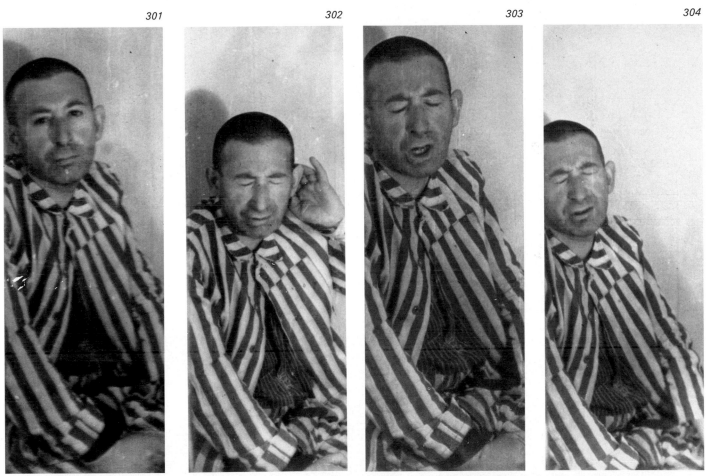

Series of photographs taken by an SS doctor during high altitude experiments

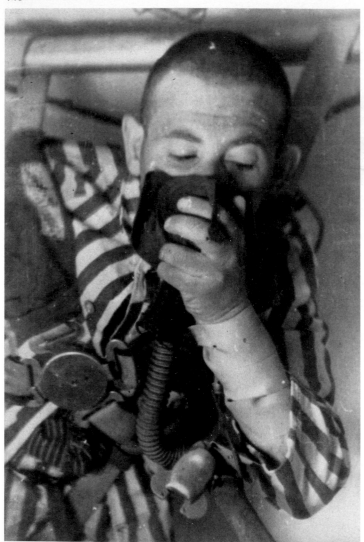

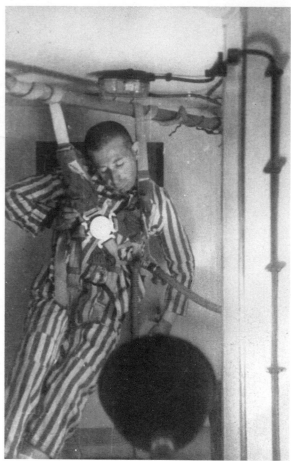

307

305

306

308

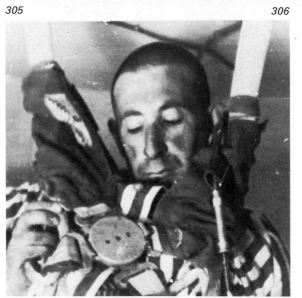

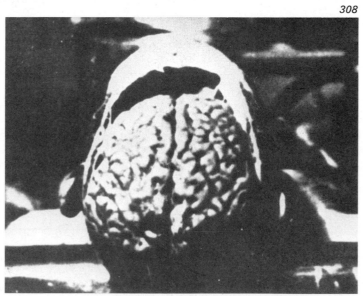

316

Nini Rascher   Munich, April 13, 1942
                                                     Trogerstr. 56

Highly esteemed, dear Reichsführer!

You have given us great pleasure once again! So many good things! The childrens' evening porridge will be enriched now for quite a while. Heinrich Peter always fidgets with excitement when a parcel arrives. He guessed who had sent it and was of course given some chocolate immediately.

Dear Reichsführer, I thank you from the bottom of my heart for the presents and the pleasure which you have given us all. My husband is very fond of chocolate and took some with him to the concentration camp.

We thought that you would allow yourself a little peace and quiet after so many strenuous weeks but you hat to leave again today.

Thank you very much, dear Reichsführer, for the letter which you enclosed!

My husband is very pleased at the interest which you have shown in his experiments. At Easter he conducted the experiments for which Dr. Romberg would have shown too much restraint and compassion, on his own. My husband will discuss all these matters with Mr. Sievers at the end of the month.

My husband takes the liberty of sending his humble good wishes and of expressing his gratitude for everything.

With most sincere wishes for your wellbeing I remain

                                         Always gratefully yours
                                         Nini Rascher

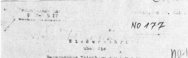

312

311

The Reichsführer SS
Reichsdoctor SS and Police
Tgb. Nr . . .   Berlin W 15, June 28, 1944
                                 Knesebeckstr. 50/51

Re: Experiments in concentration camps by the Chief of
       the Air Force Health Service.
       Orders RF SS May 15, 1944
Enclosures: —1—

                                                    SECRET

Reichsführer!

The Chief of the Air Force Health Service requests in the enclosed GKdo-letter permission to carry out experiments on
prisoners to examine two simple but promising methods of
making sea water drinkable.

2) SS Gruppenführer Glücks
With reference to the above letter it is hereby stated that there
exists absolutely no objection to the experiments proposed by
the Chief of the Air Force Health Service which are to be carried out in the Rascher department in the Dachau concentration camp. Where possible, Jews or quarantine prisoners
should be used.
I take the liberty of questioning SS Group leader Nebe's sug-
gestion that gypsies should be used in these experiments as
their different racial make-up could produce results which are
not absolutely applicable to our men.
For this reason it would be desirable, if possible, to use
prisoners who are racially comparable to the European
population. I obediently request approval so that the experiments can begin.

                                 Heil Hitler!
                                 Grawitz

Notes from the conference on the processing of salt water for
human consumption on May 20, 1944

Participants:

. . .

In the opinion of the Chief of the Medical Service this series of
experiments is expected to result in permanent injuries or
death for the experimental subjects concerned. Therefore the
persons provided by the Reichsführer SS should be used for
this purpose . . .

313

Reichsführer SS
Reichsdoctor SS and Police

Berlin W 15, Knesebeckstr. 50/54

Sub: Bio-chemical treatment of sepsis etc, with bio-chemical medicaments

To the
Reichsführer SS Heinrich Himmler
Berlin SW 11
Prinz Albrechtstr. 8

Reichsführer!

I take the liberty of submitting the following intermediary reports on the results of the bio-chemical treatment of sepsis and other cases of illness:
During the time reported 40 cases were bio-chemically treated in the Dachau SS infirmary. Apart from sepsis other cases of illness were treated where it was thought that the use of bio-chemical medicaments promised a decisive change for the better.

Phlegmonous-Purulent processes	17
Sepsis	8
Furnucles and abcesses	2
Infected operation wounds	1
Malaria	5
Pleural empyema	3
Septic Endocarditis	1
Nephrosis	1
Chronic sciatica	1
Gallstones	1

Most cases of sepsis were artificially induced. It has been ascertained so far that bio-chemical treatment has hardly any effect in serious cases. All sepsis cases ended fatally. The malaria cases were completely unaffected.
Finally, it remains to be said that from a total of 40 cases one result was positive and four were dubious, against 35 failures of which 10 ended fatally. The experiments in Dachau are to be continued.

signed: Grawitz

315

The Chief of the Air Force Medical Service
Az: 55 Nr. 510/44 g. Kdos. (2f)   Saalow, June 7, 1944
To the
Minister of the Interior and Reichsführer SS
via Medical Chief SS and Police
Berlin W
Knesebeckstr. 51

Honourable Minister!

You once gave the Air Force the opportunity to solve urgent medical problems by carrying out experiments on human beings. Today I am once again faced with a problem which still remains unsolved even after numerous experiments on animals and volunteer test persons.
40 healthy experimental subjects are required for a period of four weeks. Dachau concentration camp would be most suitable for this purpose as previous experiments have shown that it has the necessary laboratory equipment.

314

(Taken from the indictment)

A third type of experiment was the so-called phlegmone experiment. These experiments were conducted between the years 1942 and 1943 on orders from Himmler.

. . .

Healthy people were selected who were then infected with pus taken from a phlegmone patient.

. . .

The majority of prisoners used for these experiments were clergymen of all nationalities.

File cards, temperature charts and lab records from malaria experiments carried out on concentration camp prisoners

317

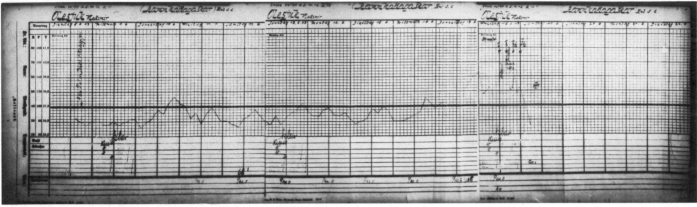

319

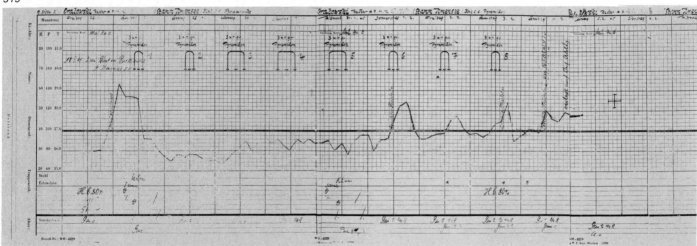

320

318

B E S C H E I N I G U N G.

Es wird hiemit bestätigt,von der Gef.Eig.Verw.
des K.L.Dachau

1 Taschenuhr weiss (Kienzle)

leihweise zu dienstlichen Zwecken empfangen zu
haben.

Dachau,den 23.Okt.1943.

Prof. Claus Schilling

321

MALARIA - AUSWEIS.

ausgestellt am: 23 März 1945   194

Kontrolle

Der SS P Häftling, Nr. 100707

Name: Gajda Franz

ist in Malaria-Beobachtung.

MALARIA-LABORATORIUM
Dachau 3 K   DACHAU 3K
R E V I E R .

322

323

324

Concentration Camp Dachau   Dachau, November, 20, 1944
3K—Malaria Dept.

Confidential

Report on the preparation Boehringer 2516
...The "Krankengut" (quota of sick persons) consisted of 66 adults...

                                    signed: Prof. Dr. Claus Schilling

325

Copy

Radio Station, Dachau Concentration Camp
received   April 5, 1945 at 9.35 p.m.

To the   from Oranienburg
Commandant of Dachau Concentration Camp

Prof. Schilling's series of experiments is to be stopped immediately by order of RF SS
dated April 5, 1945.

                    signed: Glücks
                    attested copy: The SS camp doctor
                    Dachau concentration camp
                    SS-Sturmbannführer

326

Malaria Experiments
(from the U.S. Court charge sheet, Dachau trial)

A series of experiments concerning the treatment of malaria were conducted under
the supervision of the accused, Dr. Schilling.

Schilling requested that prisoners should be put at his disposal.
None of the 1200 selected had ever agreed to or volunteered for these experiments.
Clergymen were frequently selected for this purpose.

The prisoners were infected with malaria either through mosquito bites or through in-
jections of extract taken from the mucous glands of mosquitoes.

327

Death certificate: Pietro Mazzuco

Konzentrationslager *Überlingen a/see*
Häftlingskrankenbau   den *22. 1. 1945.*

Abgang durch Tod!

Gef. Art: *Sch.H.* Name: *Mazzuco Pietro*   Block: *1* Nr: *113415*

geboren: *21. 2. 1892.* zu *Cairo Montenotte* Beruf: *Bauer*

Fam. Stand: *verh.*   Kinder: *fünf*   Relig.: r.k.   Ital.

Wohnort: Cengia, Villa della Bernida

Einweisende Dienststelle: *Befehlshaber der Sipo. u.des SD in Verona/Italien.*

Revieraufnahme: Gestorben: *22. 1. 1945.*

Leichenschau: *24.I.45*   Zeit: *14 · 13⁰⁰*

Diagnose: *Allgemeine Schwäche*

Todesursache: *Vermutlich Kreislaufschwäche*

Der Lagerarzt

333

Death certificate: Zbigniew Wojtaziewicz

Konzentrationslager Dachau   den 6.Februar 1945
Häftlingskrankenbau

Abgang durch Tod!

Zbigniew

Gef. Art: Sch. Name: W o j t a s i e w i c z   Block: 30 Nr.: 107 539

geboren: 29.7.90   zu Kielce   Beruf: Dolmetscher

Fam. Stand: verh.   Kinder: 1   Relig.: rk. Pole

Wohnort: Warschau

Einweisende Dienststelle:

Revieraufnahme: 5.2.45   Gestorben: 6.Februar 1945 um 8.- Uhr

Leichenschau: 6.Februar 1.45   Zeit: um 14.-Uhr

Diagnose: Gehirnblutung

Todesursache: Versagen von Herz und Kreislauf bei Gehirnblutung.

Der Lagerarzt

SS-Sturmbannführer

KL./37/4.43 See.000

334

Howl with the wolves you must (1943/58) *339*   The Informer (1943/61) *340*

Speak up now if you can
("Resistance", 1933/58)

341

Speculating on heroic death
("Resistance", 1934)

342

343

"Shot while trying to escape"

Prisoners are compelled to play music while escorting a condemned fellow-prisoner to his execution.   *344*

SS-Wirtschaftsverwaltungshauptamt
Amtsgruppe D
– Concentration Camps –
D 171 Az.: 14 f I/Ot/S
Geheim Tgb.-Nr. 57/43

Oranienburg January 22, 1943

SECRET

Sub: Regulations for executions

Ref: Order from the Chief of the Sipo
and the SD - IV D 2 c - 450/42 g – 81
– of Jan 14, 1943

Encl: – 1 –

Enclosed is a copy of the newly revised regulations for executions which are to be strictly observed.

With reference to No III § g of the regulations it is ordered that a copy of the execution order and execution report should be sent to this office as before. The previous regulations regarding executions are to be returned to this office immediately.

With regard to the carrying out of death sentences on women the Reichsführer SS und Chief of the German Police, has ordered that German women be handed over to the judicial authorities for execution and that foreign women should be executed in a simplified manner as with Soviet Russians and Jews. The Reichsführer SS wishes that the condemned women should not learn of the proposed discharge of the death penalty beforehand.

In future the above order of the Reichsführer SS is to be observed.

Chief of the Central Office
SS-Obersturmbannführer

345

SS-Wirtschafts-Verwaltungshauptamt　　　　Oranienburg, den 22. Januar 1943.
Amtsgruppe D
– Konzentrationslager –
D I/1 /Az.: 14 f I/Ot/S.-
Geheim Tgb.-Nr. 57/43 .

Betreff: Durchführungsbestimmungen für Exekutionen.
Bezug: Erlaß des Chefs der Sipo und des SD -IV D 2 c-
450/42 g. -81- vom 14.1.43.
Anlagen: -1-

15 Ausfertigungen .

An die
Lagerkommandanten der
Konzentrationslager

Geheime Reichssache

Da., Sah., Bu., Au., Flo., Neu., Ra., Gr.-Ro., Natz.,
Nie., Stu., Rav., Herz. und Kriegsgef.-Lager Lublin.

Anliegend wird ein Abdruck der neugefaßten Durchführungsbestimmungen für Exekutionen zur genauesten Beachtung übersandt.

Zu Ziffer III Abs. g dieser Bestimmungen wird befohlen, daß Abschrift der Exekutionsanordnung und Exekutionsprotokoll wie bisher der hiesigen Dienststelle zu übersenden sind.

Die bisher gültigen Durchführungsbestimmungen für Exekutionen sind sofort hierher zurückzugeben.

Der Reichsführer-SS und Chef der Deutschen Polizei hat hinsichtlich der Vollstreckung von Todesurteilen gegen Frauen angeordnet, daß deutsche Frauen der Justiz zur Vollstreckung zu übergeben sind und die Vollstreckung des Todesurteils gegen ausländische Frauen im vereinfachten Verfahren wie bei Sowjetrussen und Juden erfolgen soll. Der Reichsführer-SS wünscht, daß die verurteilten Frauen von dem beabsichtigten Vollzug der Todesstrafe vorher nichts merken.

In Zukunft ist nach dem vorstehenden Befehl des Reichsführers-SS zu verfahren.

Der Chef des Zentralamtes

SS - Obersturmbannführer

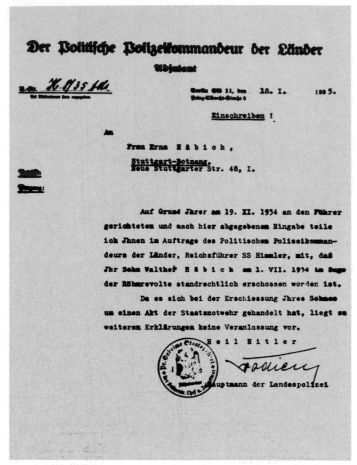

346

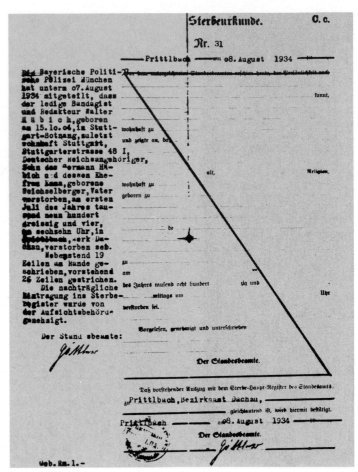

347

Death certificate: Walter Häbich

The Commander of the Federal Political Police
—Adjutant—

Berlin SW 11, Jan 18, 1935
Registered!

Mrs. Erna Häbich
Stuttgart-Botnang
Neue Stuttgarter Str. 48/I

With regard to your petition of Nov 19, 1934 to the Führer
which was later directed to this office—I wish to inform you on
behalf of the Commander of the Federal Political Police,
Reichsführer SS Himmler, that your son Walther Häbich was
court martialled and shot on July 1, 1934 as a consequence of
the Röhm uprising. Your son was shot in an act of justifiable
homicide in defence of the State. This requires no further explanation.

Heil Hitler!
Captain of the Federal Political Police

Invalid transports to Hartheim Castle near Linz. Ruthless exploitation and insufficient nourishment resulted in many prisoners becoming unfit for work within a very short time. In 1942, 3166 of them were sent in so-called invalid transports to Hartheim Castle near Linz to be gassed.

348 Hartheim castle near Linz/Danube

On the occasion of the 50th anniversary of the reign of His Imperial Regal Apostolic Majesty Emperor Franz Joseph I His Highness Prince Camillo Heinrich Starhemberg dedicates this asylum to the poor feeble-minded and imbeciles, idots and cretins in the year 1898.

349

Copy

No. 471   Hartheim, June 15, 1940

The carpenter Ottmar Holzheu, Catholic, domiciled in Hart-heim, Akoven/Oberdonau died in his appartment on June 15, 1940 at 5.45 a. m.

The deceased was born on September 12, 1905 in Munich.

Father: Alois Holzheu–lift operator.

Mother: Anna Holzheu–née Sandl.

The deceased was not married.

Registered on the basis of a report by the Director of the Hartheim State Institution.

      The Registrar
      Wirth

Cause of death: tuberculosis of the lungs

It is hereby certified that the above transcript conforms with the entry in the death registrar.

The accuracy of this transcript is certified by ...

350

State Institution Hartheim   Hartheim June 16, 1940
LB—137   Linz/Danube P.O.B. 324
Tgb. Nr. 540   Tel. Alkoven 9

Mr. Alois Holzheu
Lift Operator
München
Hefnerstr. 6/0

Dear Mr. Holzheu!

It is our sad duty to inform you that your son Mr. Ottmar Holzheu who was recently admitted to our institution on a ministerial order according to the instructions of the Defence Kommissar of the Reich, died unexpectedly on June 15, 1940 from tuberculosis of the lungs. Unfortunately all medical efforts to save your son's life were of no avail.

As the type and severity of your son's ailment gave no hope for recovery and subsequent discharge, his death can only be regarded as a deliverance which freed him from suffering and life long institution care. We hope that this assurance may prove to be of some consolation to you.

To avoid the risk of an epidemic, the danger of which has become especially great during the war, your son was cremated immediately in accordance with police instructions.

Should you wish the urn containing your son's remains to be buried in a particular cemetery—the transfer of the urn is free of charge—we request that you send written consent to the administration of the cemetery in question. In the event that you do not make such a request within the next 14 days the urn will be buried elsewhere. We enclose two death certificates which you should keep in a safe place as they may be required by the administrative authorities.

2 Encl.   Seal of the   Heil Hitler!
    Hartheim State Institution   Dr. Steiner

The accuracy of this transcript is certified by:

351

352

Plan of Hartheim Castle

Lfd.Nr.	Name	Vorname	Geb.Dat.	Häftl.Nr.	Nation2l.	Transp.Liste Nr.

K.L.Mauthausen/Unterkunft Gusen. Gusen,den 3.Dezember 1941.

Liste der am 3.12.41 nach KL.Dachau/Krankensanatorium überstellten Häftlinge!

1	Albelate-Pequerell	Blas	3.2.88	8978	Spanier	9
2	Avino-Ventura	Jose	24.2.95	10749	Spanier	11
3	Baranyai	Frans	19.10.11	12505	AZR/Deutscher	17
4	Borkowski	Kasimir	20.2.07	1164	P-Schutz	16
5	Burkacki	Kasimir	6.10.19	7456	P-Schutz	8
6	Cabello-Cabello	Juan	26.11.11	9860	Spanier	7
7	Camprubi-Selles	Ramon	23.12.02	11575	Spanier	8
8	Cano-Espejo	Benito	6.6.11	10873	Spanier	7
9	Chyzewski	Hipolit	7.8.04	3467	Pole	10
10	Ciechowski	Alex	13.2.03	5011	Pole	7
11	Cogollos-Giner	Ramon	23.12.11	10388	Spanier	13
12	Csekajewski	Heinrich	4.1.01	6079	Pole	7
13	Dabrowski	Witold	9.3.13	3499	Pole	9
14	Fatsini-Fontcuberta	Jose	12.12.85	9897	Spanier	9
15	Galvan-Pereda	Franz	27.4.96	10717	Spanier	7
16	Glowka	Josef	10.3.10	8400	Pole	7
17	Gorecki	Felix	15.12.98	1516	Pole	15
18	Gracia-Casabona	Lorenzo	29.5.23	9320	Spanier	17
19	Grochowski v.Kosowski	Zenon	18.10.06	6242	Pole	10
20	Gross	Moritz	18.3.21	7531	Poln.Jude	14
21	Groszewski	Wenzel	1.1.96	8035	Pole	9
22	Horvath	Michael	10.9.95	8438	AZR/Deutscher	7
23	Juncosa-Pascual	Ramon	29.6.12	10804	Spanier	11
24	Juretzko	Wilhelm	28.9.89	348	Pole	9
25	Karkowski	Marian	23.7.95	6393	Pole	7
26	Kopczynski	Siegmund	26.11.14	3908	Pole	10
27	Kopec	Josef	19.7.10	6472	Pole	7
28	Kosak	Michael	1.10.01	1797	Pole	16
29	Kozlowski	Ladisl.	24.11.83	1808	Pole	7
30	Kresnicki	Josef	14.3.91	463	Pole	7
31	Larrea-Bertis	Marzel	24.5.17	11789	Spanier	10
32	Lasak	Stefan	22.11.04	5372	Pole	7
33	Lazaro-Torres	Segundo	12.1.17	11736	Spanier	11
34	Lesinski	Heinrich	13.7.06	8570	Pole	7
35	Lubelfeld	Alfred	19.4.06	5906	Poln.Jude	14
36	Maduell-Muto	Juan	30.11.12	12164	Spanier	11
37	Marosek	Stefan	15.7.09	8105	Pole	9
38	Marques-Mateos	Juan	7.1.19	3960	Spanier	11
39	Moreno-Mora	Antonio	12.8.10	6485	Spanier	9
40	Masyl	Franz	3.9.14	5499	Pole	9
41	Navarro-Bague	Amalio	21.1.96	6491	Spanier	12
42	Navarro-Couse	Jose	14.3.11	6550	Spanier	11
43	Orus-Morillo	Pascual	...4.04	6696	Spanier	12
44	Pareno-Castillo	Franz	11.7.13	10694	Spanier	7
45	Perez-Baena	Antonio	7.3.10	6961	Spanier	7
46	Pietrzak	Josef	18.3.06	6774	Pole	16
47	Pilak	Michael	18.4.17	6727	Pole	12
48	Popiele	Leo	6.4.85	2611	Pole	15
49	Porra-Sanchez	Franz	6.2.15	6960	Spanier	12
50	Pina-Barrera	Manuel	8.9.03	10000	Spanier	9
51	Roca-Berjea	Antonio	22.9.22	9027	Spanier	7
52	Rogalski	Eugen	21.3.03	8178	Pole	8
53	Segovia-Toledo	Franz	17.7.10	9697	Spanier	8
54	Soto-Gonzalez	Franz	29.1.17	9719	Spanier	12
55	Valls-Munich	Antonio	10.5.15	6756	Spanier	12
56	Vermaut-Hibbo	Joaquin	8.1.90	10260	Spanier	10
57	Vrtnig	Johann	27.5.92	11156	BV/Deutscher	7
58	Zakrzewski	Bruno	3.2.10	8348	Pole	8
59	Ziobinski	Adam	8.11.95	7372	Pole	11
60	Aguilar-Vera	Rafael	12.8.02	9003	Spanier	12

353

Dachau sanatorium did not exist.
This transport never arrived. The prisoners were registered as "dead" in Mauthausen. They were gassed in Hartheim Castle.

To the
Commandants of the Concentration Camps
Dachau, Sachsenhausen, Buchenwald, Mauthausen, Auschwitz, Flossenbürg, Gross-Rosen, Neuengamme, Niederhagen.

As the commandants of the concentration camps Dachau, Sachsenhausen, Buchenwald, Mauthausen und Auschwitz have been informed in the letter already referred to, a medical commission is to visit the aforementioned camps in the near future to select prisoners. It is planned to carry out this inspection in the concentration camps of Flossenbürg, Gross-Rosen, Neuengamme and Niederhagen during the first half of January 1942 ...
Enclosed is a specimen of the registration form to be used so that preliminary work can begin. These forms are to be duplicated and completed.
The question regarding incurable physical illnesses should, where possible, be answered with a short diagnosis and not simply with the words yes or no. Apart from this the question of war injuries is to be ascertained as it is of great help to the medical commission in their examination work ...
All existing files and medical records are to be made available to the medical commission upon request ...
A report is to be made to the "Inspecteur der Konzentrationslager" upon completion of the examination and should contain the number of prisoners who are to receive "Sonderbehandlung" '14 f 13'. You will be informed as to the exact time of arrival of the medical commission in good time.

signed: Liebehenschel
SS-Obersturmbannführer

354

NC-2799

EIDESSTATTLICHE ERKLAERUNG

Ich, Dr. Julius MUTHIG, schwoere, sage aus und erklaere:

1.) Ich bin am 9. Mai 1908 in Aschaffenburg am Main (Deutschland) geboren. Ich besuchte die Volksschule von 1914 bis 1918 in Aschaffenburg, anschliessend bis 1927 die Oberrealschule in Aschaffenburg. Von 1927 bis zu meinem Staatsexamen am 6. Dezember 1934 besuchte ich die Universitaet Wuerzburg, mit Ausnahme des Sommer-Semesters im Jahre 1932, welches ich in Innsbruck verbrachte. Ich studierte Medizin. Von Januar 1935 bis Dezember 1935 war ich Medizinischer Praktikant am Thueringischen Landeskrankenhaus Sondershausen. Vom 1. Januar 1936 bis 20. Oktober 1937 war ich Assistenz-Arzt im gleichen Krankenhaus. Von 21. Oktober 1937 bis 31. Dezember 1938 war ich praktischer Arzt in Grossenehrich. Vom 1. Januar 1939 bis zu meiner Einberufung zur Waffen-SS am 23. oder 26. November 1939 war ich praktischer Arzt in Holzhen/Thueringen.

2.) Am 1. April 1932 trat ich in die NSDAP ein. Meine Parteinummer war ungefaehr 9651000. Im Juni 1933 trat ich der SS bei und erhielt die Nummer 104518. Ich war Mitglied der NSV und dem NS-Aerztebund.

3.) Nach meiner militaerischen Ausbildungszeit in der Waffen-SS im Dezember 1939 und Januar 1940, wurde ich am 8. Februar 1940 nach dem Konzentrationslager Dachau als Lagerarzt kommandiert. Ich war dort bis Juli 1940 als Arzt im Revier taetig. Im Juli 1940 wurde ich nach dem Konzentrationslager Hamburg-Neuengamme versetzt und war dort als Standort-Arzt bis April 1941 taetig. Von 1. April 1941 bis Februar 1942 wurde ich als erster Lager-Arzt nach dem Konzentrationslager Dachau kommandiert. Im Februar 1942 bis Juli 1942 war ich erster Lager-Arzt im Konzentrationslager Oranienburg. Vom Juli 1942 bis zum Zusammenbruch Deutschlands war ich als Truppenarzt der Waffen-SS taetig.

4.) Im Herbst 1941 bei einem dienstlichen Besuch des Dr. Lolling in meinem Revier wurde mir von ihm mitgeteilt, dass in kurzer Zeit eine Kommission aus 4 Aerzten bestehend unter der Leitung von Prof. Heyde des Konzentrationslager Dachau besuchen wuerde. Die Aufgabe dieser Kommission sei die, arbeitsunfaehige KZ-Haeftlinge zur Verlegung zwecks Euthanasie zu erfassen und sie nach dem Konzentrationslager Mauthausen zur Vergasung zu verlegen. Kurze Zeit nach dieser Besprechung mit Dr. Lolling erschien die angemeldete Kommission. Sie bestand aus 4 Psychiatern und die Leitung dieser Kommission hatte Prof. Heyde, der auch selbst dabei war. Ich selbst, sowie die anderen Lager-Aerzte des Konzentrationslagers Dachau, hatten mit der Kommission sowie deren Arbeit nichts zu tun. Ich sah aber, wie diese 4 Aerzte zwischen 2 Baracken an 4 getrennte Tische sassen um viele Hunderte von KZ-Haeftlinge waren vor ihnen angetreten um einzeln zu irgend-einem der Aerzte herantreten. Dort wurden die einzelnen KZ-Haeftlinge an Hand ihrer Arbeitsunfaehigkeit und ihrer politischen Akte ueberprueft und dementsprechend ausgesucht. Ich weiss, dass diese Kommission sich nur wenige Tage in Dachau aufhielt und dass es ihnen unmoeglich war, diese vielen KZ-Haeftlinge in dieser kurzen Zeit medizinisch zu untersuchen. Die Untersuchung bestand lediglich in der Ueberpruefung der Akte im Beisein des betreffenden KZ-Haeftlings. Es handelte sich hier um Haeftlinge maennlicher deutscher Staatsangehoerigkeit und Staatsangehoerige anderer Nationen, Juden usw. Ich kann mit absoluter Bestimmtheit sagen, dass Prof. Heyde diese Aktion leitete und selbst dabei war, jedoch sind mir die Namen der anderen Aerzte entfallen.

5.) Einige Wochen, nachdem diese Kommission das Konzentrationslager Dachau verliess, im Dezember 1941, ging der erste Transport von mehreren Hunderten KZ-Haeftlingen, die von der Psychiatern ausgesucht waren, nach der Konzentrationslager Mauthausen zwecks Vergasung ab. Ein weiterer Transport ebenfalls von der Kommission ausgesuchten KZ-Haeftlingen welche auch aus mehreren Hunderten bestand, gingen im Januar 1942 nach dem Konzentrationslager Mauthausen ab. Ob weitere Transporte erfolgten, kann ich nicht beschwoeren, da ich kurz nach dem zweiten Transport aus dem Konzentrationslager Dachau versetzt wurde. Die Aktion zur Erfassung von Arbeitsunfaehigen zur Euthanasie im Konzentrationslager war mir nur bekannt unter dem Namen " AKTION HEYDE ".

Ich habe diese Erklaerung mit meinem aus 2 Seiten in der deutschen Sprache geben und erklaere, dass es nach meinem besten Wissen und Glauben die volle Wahrheit ist. Ich hatte Gelegenheit Aenderungen und Berichtigungen in obiger Erklaerung vorzunehmen und diese habe ich freiwillig gemacht, ohne jeglichen Vorzug oder Belohnung und bin unter keinerlei Zwang oder Drohung ausgesetzt.

....
Julius MUTHIG

Before me, Mr. Fred Rodell, US Civilian AGO Identification # D 432576 Interrogator Evidence Division, Office of Chief of Counsel for War Crimes, appeared JULIUS MUTHIG to me known, who in my presence signed the foregoing statement (Eidesstattliche Erklaerung) consisting of two (2) pages in the German language, and swore that the same was true. On the 16th of April 1947.

....
FRED RODELL
US Civ AGO - D 432576

Affidavit

I, Dr. Julius Muthig, make the following statement under oath:

4) In the autumn of 1941, on the occasion of a duty inspection of my infirmary by Dr. Lolling, he told me that a commission of 4 doctors led by Professor Heyde would shortly be visiting Dachau camp. The commission's task was to select prisoners unfit for work to be subjected to euthanasia and transferred to Mauthausen concentration camp to be gassed. Shortly after my conversation with Dr. Lolling the commission duly arrived. It consisted of 4 psychiatrists and was led by Professor Heyde, who was also present. I and the other camp doctors had nothing to do with the commission or its work. However, I saw these doctors sit at four separate tables placed between two of the huts and hundreds of prisoners being made to stand in front of one of the four. The prisoners were being examined and selected according to their unsuitability for work and their political records. I know that this commission spent only a few days in Dachau and that it was impossible to carry out a medical examination on so many prisoners in such a short space of time. The examination consisted simply of checking the records in the presence of the prisoner concerned. The prisoners examined were males of German and other nationalities, Jews etc. I can state categorically that Professor Heyde directed the operation and that he was present in person, but I have forgotten the names of the other doctors.

5) A few weeks after the commission had left Dachau, in December 1941 the first trainload of several hundred prisoners selected by the psychiatrists' commission left for Mauthausen concentration camp to be gassed. Another trainload of prisoners selected by the commission and also containing several hundred prisoners left in January 1942 for Mauthausen.

I cannot say whether other trainloads followed because I was posted from Dachau shortly after the second trainload. The operation for selecting those unfit for work and for euthanasia was known in Dachau concentration camp as "Aktion Heyde".

I have read the above statement consisting of two pages in the German language and swear that it is, to the best of my knowledge, the truth. I was given the opportunity to change and correct the above statement. I made this statement of my own free will without duress or threat and without the promise of a reward of any kind.

Julius Muthig

Before me, Mr. Fred Rodall, US Civilian AGO Identification D 43 576 Interrogator Evidence Division, Office of Chief of Counsel for War Crimes, appeared JULIUS MUTHIG known to me who in my presence signed the foregoing statement (Eidesstattliche Erklärung) consisting of two (2) pages in the German language, and swore that the same was true. On the 16th of April 1947.

Fred Rodell
US Civ AGO

Dr. med. Sigmund Rascher

München, Trogerstr.56, den 9. August 42.

Hochverehrter Reichsführer !

°............

Wie Sie wißen, wird im KL Dachau dieselbe Einrichtu
wie in Linz gebaut. Nachdem die"Invalidentransporte" sowieso in
bestimmten Kammern enden, frage ich, ob nicht in diesen Kammern an den
sowieso dazu bestimmten Personen die Wirkung unserer verschiedenen
Kampfgase erprobt werden kann ? Bis jetzt liegen nur Tierversuche
bezw. Berichte über Unfälle bei Herstellung dieser Gase vor.
Wegen dieses Absatzes schicke ich den Brief als"Geheimsache.".

....

mit gehorsamster Grüssen
und Heil Hitler
bin ich Ihr dankbarst ergebenster
S. Rascher.

356

Dr. Sigmund Rascher   Munich
                             Trogerstr. 56, August 9, 1942

Esteemed Reichsführer!

......

As you know, the same installation as in Linz is to be built in Dachau. As the "invalid transports"
terminate in the special chambers anyway I wondered if it would be possible to test the effects of
our different combat gases in theses chambers using the persons who are destined for those
chambers anyway. The only reports which are available so far are of experiments on animals or of
accidents which occured in the manufacture of the gases.
Because of this paragraph I am marking this letter "Secret".

....
                                        Your obedient servant
                                        Heil Hitler!
                                        S. Rascher

357

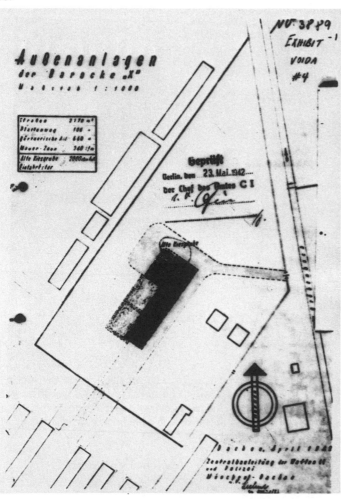

358

Zentralbauleitung der
Waffen-SS und Polizei
München-Dachau

Erläuterungsbericht

zum Baumittelantrag über den Neubau des Gebäudes "x"
im KL. Dachau

1. Dienstliche Veranlassung:

wird nachgereicht.

2. Beschaffenheit der Baustelle:

Wie aus den beigefügten Lageplan ersichtlich ist, liegt der für das Gebäude "x" vorgesehene Bauplatz im Bereich des SS-Lagers Dachau auf dem bewaldeten Gelände zwischen bestehenden Krematorium und dem Baulager der hiesigen Dienststelle. Entwässerungsleitung ist auf der Baustelle vorhanden. Der Anschluß an die Bewässerungsleitung sowie an das elektrische Stromnetz bietet keine besonderen Schwierigkeiten. Der Baustelle ist eben.

3. Baugrund:

Die Beschaffenheit des Baugrundes ist gut. Unter der Humusdecke kommt der in dieser Formation übliche, sandige Kiesboden. Der Kies- bzw. Sandaushub kann größtenteils für die Bauarbeiten wieder verwendet werden. Der höchste Grundwasserspiegel liegt ca. bei - 1,50 m.

4. Entwurfsanordnung:

Die Planunterlagen werden von der Zentralbauleitung der Waffen-SS und Polizei München-Dachau, nach dem Vorschlag des Hauptamtes in Berlin ausgearbeitet. Das Gebäude ist fast von allen Seiten von Bäumen umgeben und steht daher verhältnismäßig isoliert im Gelände. Es wird von einer ca. 2,0 m hohen undurchsichtigen Mauer umgeben. Die Zufahrt zu dem Gebäude erfolgt einerseits vom KL. aus durch das bestehende Tor beim jetzigen Krematorium, andererseits vom SS-Barackenlager I aus. Das Gebäude wird nur für die Heizzentrale und das dazugehörige Kohlenlager unterkellert. Im Erdgeschoß befinden sich die verlangten Räume und Anlagen. Der Dachraum wird nicht ausgebaut, ist aber in der Mitte auf einem 80 cm breiten Steg begehbar. Die Fundamente bestehen aus Stampfbeton. Das Mauerwerk wird in Ziegelsteinen hochgeführt. Die Fußböden werden je nach ihrer Beanspruchung in Beton-, Fliesenbelag oder Holz ausgeführt (siehe Erdgeschoßplan). Das Dach erhält freitragende Binder mit Balkendecke. Wärmeisolierung aus Glaswolle, die auf der Deckenschalung liegt. Das Dach wird mit Flachpfannen eingedeckt. Decken und Innenwände werden glatt verputzt. Raum Nr. 8 erhält eine Eisenbetonzwischendecke. Die Außenfront erhält Münchener Rauhputz. Als Heizung ist Niederdruckdampfheizung vorgesehen, mit eigener Station im Untergeschoß des Gebäudes. Als Feuerschutz werden Schaumfeuerlöscher in genügender Anzahl bereitgestellt. Die Be- und Entwässerung sowie die Lichtleitung wird an das bestehende Be- und Entwässerungs- bzw. Stromnetz angeschlossen.

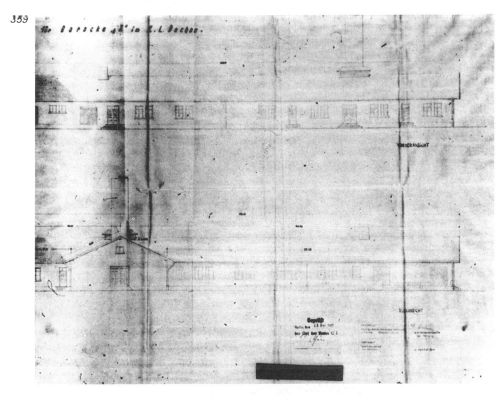

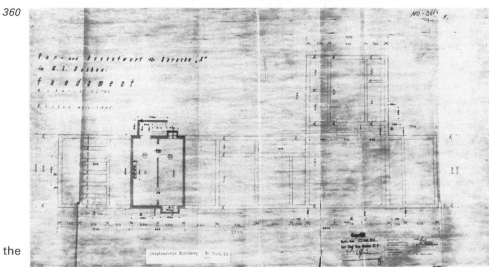

Plans and preliminary report for the
construction of the crematorium.

361

Mortuary in the crematorium

362

SS-Wirtschafts-Verwaltungshauptamt

Berlin, 23. Juli 1942

Geheim!

C V /1-480 A Geheim-13/42/Ld Bm/Wt.

Betr.: KL Dachau X-Baracke
Bezug: Antrag der Bauleitung vom 27.4.1942
Anlg.: 1 Bauantrag Erstschrift

An die
Zentralbauleitung der
Waffen- und Polizei
München - Dachau

Baubefehl Nr.137

Auf Grund der vorgelegten Unterlagen und in Erweiterung des Baubefehls Nr.196 befehle ich die endgültige Durchführung der Arbeiten für die X-Baracke im KL Dachau.

Ich bemerke hierzu:

1.) Das Bauwerk befindet sich innerhalb des vom GB-Bau unter der Kennummer V II/U p a l genehmigten Bauvolumens für das KL Dachau.

2.) Der Bauantrag wurde in bautechnischer, fachtechnischer und bauwirtschaftlicher Hinsicht geprüft. Die Prüfungsbemerkungen sind zu beachten.

3.) Die erforderlichen Baumittel wurden auf RM 200.000,-- festgelegt.'; Als 2.Baurate wird ein Betrag von

RM 150.000.--

zur Verfügung gestellt. Die Verrechnung erfolgt bei Kap.21/7b (Bau) 7. Die auszahlungsanweisende Baudienststelle, die Bauinspektion, muss über obigen Betrag eine Haushaltsüberwachungsliste führen. Der Leiter der Bauinspektion haftet für Auszahlungen oder Zahlungsverpflichtungen, die über den zugewiesenen Betrag hinausgehen. Vor Verwendung der restlichen 10 v.H. der zugewiesenen Mittel ist dem Amt C V zu melden, daß die ange-

wiesenen Baumittel zur Deckung aller in Frage kommenden Ausgaben ausreichen, andernfalls ist ein begründeter Nachantrag zu stellen.

4.) Die erforderlichen Kontingente sind bereits durch Sonderzuteilung bereitgestellt. Sollten noch kontingentpflichtige Rohstoffe erforderlich sein, so ist dem Amt C V ein eingehend begründeter Antrag vorzulegen.

5.) Die Arbeiten sind in der Durchführung und sind so zu fördern, daß die Inbetriebnahme der Anlagen terminmäßig gewährleistet ist. Der Baufortschritt ist mir durch die monatliche Bauberichterstattung zu melden. Arbeitskräfte der freien Wirtschaft können nicht eingesetzt werden. Die erforderlichen Häftlingen werden über das Amt C V durch den Chef des Amtes D II, Oranienburg, zugewiesen.

Der Chef des Amtes C V
(Zentrale Bauinspektion)

f.d.R.

gez.Lenzer

SS-Sturmbannführer

SS-Untersturmführer

Order to commence construction of the crematorium

363

In 1940, as the death rate continued to increase, a camp crematorium with one incinerator was built. In the course of the mass extermination plan, a bigger plant with a gas chamber and 4 incinerators—the so called "Baracke X"—was quickly erected in 1942. The gas chamber, which was camouflaged as a shower room, was never put into use. Thousands of prisoners who were selected for extermination were sent to other camps or to Hartheim Castle near Linz to be gassed.

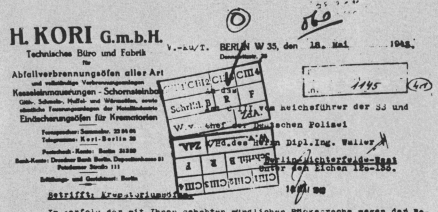

W. Müller
Engineering Office/Industrial Incinerators
Allach/München

To the
Reichsführung SS of the NSDAP
Munich
Karlstrasse   June 2, 1937

Incinerators

I thank you for your inquiry and take the liberty of offering as you requested the following incinerators:

A consultation with the commandant of Dachau concentration camp Mr. Oberführer Loritz has revealed that there is no coal gas available. I can therefore offer you a coke-fired incinerator which has proved to be very reliable.

364

H. KORI, Ltd.   Berlin W 35, May 18, 1943
Technical Office and Factory for
Refuse Incinerators of all kinds and
complete Incinerator plants
Boilers, Chimneys
Incinerators for crematoriums

To
Amt C III Reichsführer SS and
Chief of the German Police
att. of Engineer Waller
Berlin Lichterfelde West
Unter den Eichen 126—135

Re: Crematorium Incinerators

As a result of our conversation regarding the supply of a standard incinerator plant we would like to suggest our coal burning "Reform"-incinerators which have proved very successful so far. —

Plan No. 8998 shows the layout for two incinerators, whereas plan No. J 9122 shows a layout for the four incinerators already installed in Dachau.

Our estimate for the purchase of two incinerators is as follows: 1) 2 "Reform"-incinerators of the latest model with an arched coffin chamber and horizontal ash grate, including all fittings, outer door, furnace door and cleaning door, ventiles, furnace accessories, and fire-gate . . .

In the case of a second incinerator being installed the price would be reduced to RM 4.050.—.

366   Incinerators

Mass Executions

367

SS rifle range at Hebertshausen near Dachau where thousands of Soviet prisoners of war were shot

The Chief of the Sipo and the SD   Berlin, Nov 9, 1941
                                      Express!

Sub: Transport of condemned Soviet Russian prisoners of war to Dachau concentration camp
Re: none

Encl: none

The concentration camp commandants have complained that approx. 5 to 10% of the condemned Soviet Russian prisoners who come to the camp arrive dead or half dead. This fact gives the impression that the Stalags are using these transfers as a means of disposing of such prisoners.

Especially during the march from the railway station to the camp for instance a considerable number of prisoners have been seen to collapse dead or half dead from exhaustion and have to be picked up by a car following behind.

It is inevitable that the German people notice these incidents. Although these transports are usually escorted by members of the army, the general public will blame the SS for these incidents.

To avoid such incidents in future I hereby order that from now on all Soviet Russians who have already been selected as definite suspects and who are obviously dying (e. g. from hunger, typhus) and are therefore not capable of any exertion, especially marching even short distances, are to be excluded from execution transports to the concentration camps.

I request that all "Einsatzkommandos" be given corresponding instructions immediately.

368

The Reichsführer SS   Oranienburg, Nov. 15, 1941
The Inspector of the Concentration Camps
Pol./Az 14 f 14 /L Ot
Secret journal No /41

Subject: Execution of Russian Prisoners of War
Reference: none
Enclosures: none

To the Commandants of the concentration camps

Da, Sah, Bu, Mau, Flo, Neu, Au, Gr, Ro,
copy: camp doctors concentration camp officers, administration

The Reichsführer SS and Chief of the German Police fundamentally agrees with the postponement of the execution of Russian prisoners of war, (especially commissars) who, because of their physical constitution are suitable for work in a stone quarry. Prior to this, agreement must be obtained from the Chief of the Security Police and the SD.
The following order must be observed:
Upon arrival of execution transports in the camps, the camp leader and the camp doctor have to select the physically strong Russians, fit to work in a stone quarry. A list of names of the selected Russians is to be compiled in duplicate and submitted to this office.
On this list the camp doctor must state that there is medically no doubt as to the prisoners' suitability for this work.
The transfer of the said Russians to the stone quarry will be ordered from here with the approval of the Chiefs of the Security Police and the SD.

Signature
SS Brigadier and Major General
of the Waffen SS

369

Teleprint

Secret State Police
State Police Office,
Munich Teleprint–Agency

Jan 24 1942

To: Stapoleitstelle–Mr. Schimmel Munich–Secret–Urgent–
To be submitted immediately–

re: checking of Soviet prisoners of war

Up till now 2009 Soviet Russians (652 officers and 1357 men) have been selected and given special treatment, by the "Einsatzkommando" Stapoleitstelle Nürnberg–Fürth. — The prisoner of war commandant for "Wehrkreis", XIII, General Major Schemmel has been extremely cooperative. So far no difficulties whatsoever have arisen.

Stapoleitstelle Nürnberg-Fürth
signed: Otto

370

Geheime Staatspolizei
Staatspolizeileitstelle München
Fernschreib-Vermittlungsstelle

Aufgenommen Tag Monat Jahr Zeit	Raum für Eingangsstempel	Befördert Tag Monat Jahr Zeit
24 1 42 14 -- 06 von durch 1 (hs Wort unl.)		an durch
	Fernschreiben aus	Verzögerungsvermerk
FS = Nr......2024......	DR. NUERNBERG NR. 331 24.1.42 1405 = Bl.=	

AN DIE STAPOLEITSTELLE — Z. HD. H. REG. RAT SCHIMMEL MUENCHEN. ::-:: G E H E I M = D R I N G E N D. ::-:: SOFORT VORLEGEN. = BETR.: UEBERPRUEFUNG SOWJETRUSSISCHER KRIEGSGEFANGENER. — DURCH DIE EINSATZKOMMANDOS DER STAPOSTELLE NUERNBERG-FUERTH WURDEN BIS JETZT 2009 SOWJETRUSSEN (652 OFFIZIERE UND 1357 MANNSCHAFTEN) AUSGESONDERT UND DER SONDERBEHANDLUNG ZUGEFUEHRT. — DIE ZUSAMMENARBEIT MIT DEM KOMMANDEUR DER KRIEGSGEFANGENEN IM WEHRKREIS ROEM.13, GENERALMAJOR SCHEMMEL, IST AUSGEZEICHNET, SCHWIERIGKEITEN IRGENDWELCHER ART HABEN SICH BIS JETZT NICHT ERGEBEN. =
STAPOSTELLE NUERNBERG-FUERTH.
I. V. GEZ. OTTO KRIM.-RAT +

SPISOK

letesikow krasnoj armii rostrelanych w Kon.Lag. Dachau 22.2.44

LIST of

Red Army officers shot in Dachau Concentration Camp the 22. 2.44

Family name	Christ name	born
1. Fomin	Piotr	1906
2. Galkin	Nikolai	1910
3. Ignatiew	Viktor	1922
4. Ischimski	Konstantin	1920
5. Kamielow	Leonid	1921
6. Koptiew	Nikolai	1920
7. Karmalicyn	Ilja	1914
8. Kostenko	Leonid	1919
9. Lobanow	Dimitri	1914
10. Matwiejew	Georgij	1916
11. Pawlow	Wassilij	1922
12. Reszinski	Alexiej	1919
13. Siedow	Michail	1907
14. Selutin	Mikolai	1920
15. Sienkow	Piotr	1911
16. Sitnikew	Dimitri	1921
17. Smirnow	Pawel	1914
18. Wolkow	Wladimir	1922
19. Tokarew	Wassilij	1922
20. Solowiew	Jurij	1922
21. Smischlajew	Vitalij	1923
22. Semibratow	Gregorij	1918
23. Dimitin	Nikolai	1921
24. Dunow	Anatolij	1923
25. Dagomslow	Iwan	1915
26. Barabow	Salif	1920
27. Andardsanow	Iwan	1918
28. Alexiejew	Alexej	1922
29. Atamanow	Konstantin	1923
30. Amantajew	Muhamed	1922
31. Kajutin	Andrej	1914

371

SPISOK

oficerow krasnoj armii rostrelanych w Kons.Lag. Dachau 4.9.1944

LIST of

Red Army officers shot in Dachau Concentration Camp the 4th September 1944

Family name	Christ name	born	Family name	Christ name	born
1. Antonow	Nikolai	1921	46. Muri	Alexiej	1920
2. Anfierew	Wassili	1906	47. Nadrzoga	Piotr	1921
3. Anonin	Georgij	1914	48. Nikitin	Jewdokij	1900
4. Archissyn	Jefim	1918	49. Osolin	Karl	1902
5. Antoniuk	Alexander	1920	50. Panow	Wassilij	1920
6. Badoweti	Sawielij	1918	51. Pantilejew	Iwan	1920
7. Baranow	Nikolai	1901	52. Pieroew	Semion	1913
8. Baskow	Viktor	1916	53. Pietrow	Iwan	1900
9. Berkalij	Jakow	1901	54. Pietruszyn	Roman	1913
10. Bojko	Boris	1921	55. Plochotniuk	Konstantin	1925
11. Bojko	Michail	1902	56. Plochotniuk	Nikolai	1894
12. Borisienko	Wassilij	1910	57. Platonow	Grigorij	1907
13. Borisow	Stjepan	1894	58. Polosow	Siewolod	1909
14. Burda	Jakow	1923	59. Pomytkin	Pawel	1907
15. Hajrudinow	Munagid	1901	60. Resnik	Polikarp	1919
16. Christosienko	Piotr	1918	61. Siedowoj	Michail	1920
17. Cymbal	Iwan	1911	62. Sachsrow	Wassilij	1911
18. Demba	Nikolai	1922	63. Saraili	Szaliko	1919
19. Fiedotkin	Jegor	1919	64. Mieliwiorstow	Sergei	1919
20. Fiedotkin	Iwan	1915	65. Siereprekow	Pawel	1901
21. Garanin	Nikolai	1916	66. Simonienko	Stjepan	1907
22. Glodkow	Pawel	1920	67. Ginger	Michail	1886
23. Gromow	Alexander	1905	68. Sawin	Valerian	1898
24. Galin	Anatolij	1920	69. Smolowoj	Wassilij	1906
25. Gajduk	Wassilij	1924	70. Sorokounow	Unknr	1922
26. Jefimienko	Iwan	1912	71. Szalar	Siewolod	1909
27. Kalitienko	Nikita	1901	72. Szelest	Dimitri	1900
28. Astrulin	Fieder	1917	73. Ssichert	Michail	1905
29. Kalano	Boris	1917	74. Smilko	Wassilij	1922
30. Drenicki	Michail	1892	75. Starowojtow	Georgij	1906
31. Kierylenko	Alexiej	1913	76. Tarasow	Michail	1898
32. Komienko	Michail	1906	77. Tielemanow	Wladimir	1910
33. Komiuk	Mikolai	1903	78. Timryn	Alexander	1923
34. Kurbekow	Iwan	1918	79. Tkaczenko	Michail	1896
35. Kormiejew	Konstantin	1918	80. Tscherenkow	Michail	1903
36. Koslow	Wassili	1924	81. Tschernousow	Alexander	1905
37. Kortun	Boris	1908	82. Tscharnow	Grigorij	1898
38. Kuzikow	Pietr	1910	83. Tschernow	Wassilij	1926
39. Albert	Sergei	1909	84. Umow	Nikolai	1912
40. Martinienko	Alexei	1919	85. Urbanowics	Ilosiw	1892
41. Melnikow	Pietr	1913	86. Uwarow	Iwan	1920
42. Moisiejenko	Konstantin	1908	87. Waklamow	Jakow	1916
43. Grossmann	Wladimir	1915	88. Wietrow	Stjepan	1904
44. Melostan	Andrej	1904	89. Wenitschenko	Wassilij	1927
45. Morosow	Anatolij	1903	90. Kanditienko	Michail	1913

372

The Chief of the German Army Headquarters
14 n 61 WR (I 3/4)
Nr. 165/41 g   Dec 12, 1941

SECRET

Sub: Persecution of crimes against the Reich or against the occupation forces in occupied territories.

Encl: 1

For a considerable time it has been the Führer's wish that new measures should be adopted in the punishment of crimes against the Reich or the occupation forces in occupied territories. The Führer is of the opinion that for such deeds imprisonment, including life imprisonment, would be judged as a sign of weakness. An effective and lasting deterrent is only to be achieved by the death penalty, or by such measures which leave the relatives and the general public in a state of uncertainty as to the fate of the culprit. The transportation to Germany serves this purpose. The enclosed instructions for the punishment of crimes conform to the Führer's conception. They have been checked and approved by him.
                    signed: Keitel

373
The so-called "Nacht und Nebel" decree

Shot in Dachau Concentration Camp

November 1940	55 Poles
1941/1942	Thousands of Soviet Russian prisoners-of-war
February 1944	31 Soviet Russian prisoners-of-war
September 1944	90 Soviet Russian prisoners-of-war
April 1945	General Delestraint and 11 Czechoslavakian officers

Apart from these many unknown prisoners were secretly executed between 1933 and 1945.

374

"The Final Solution of the Jewish Question"

375

Auschwitz

381

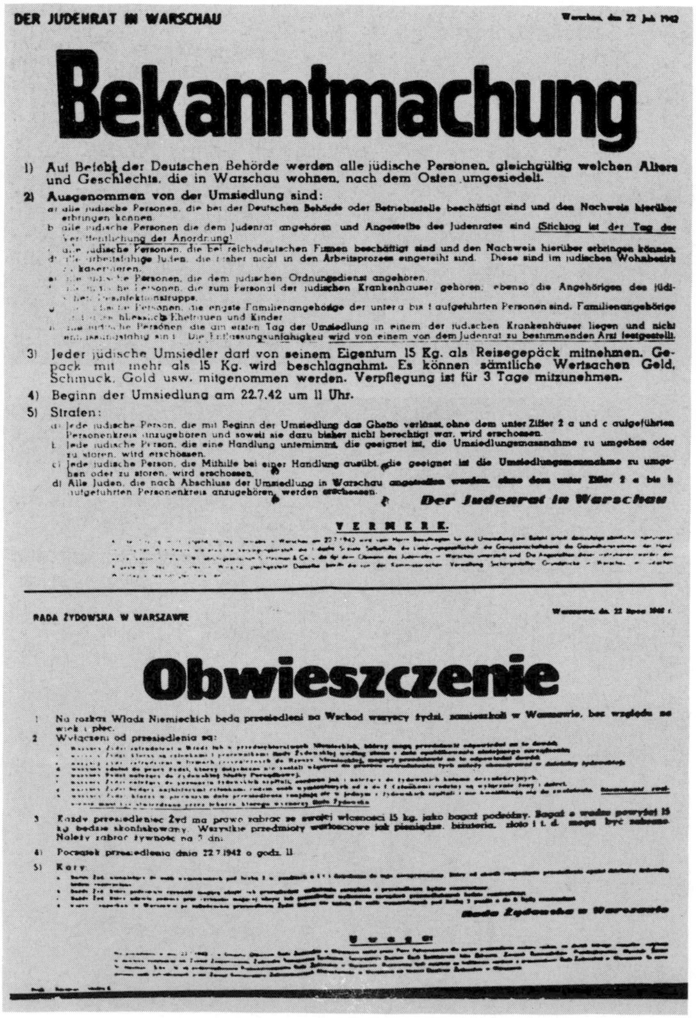

383

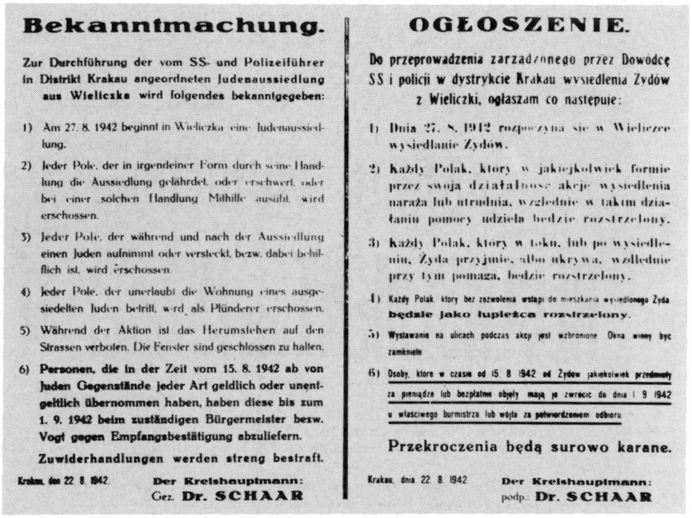

382

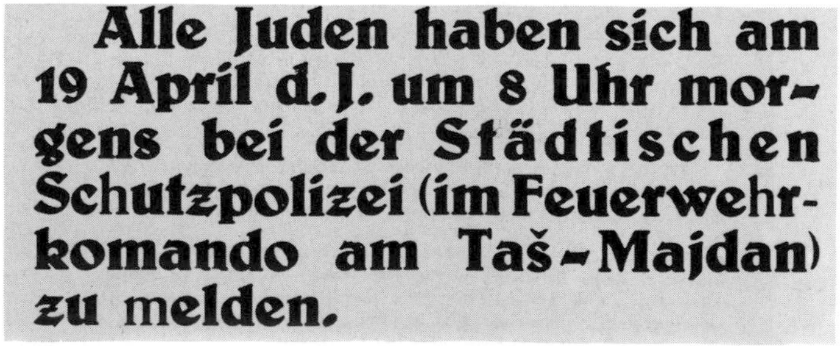

All Jews are to report to the municipal police (at the fire station Tas-Majdan) at 8 a.m. on April 19 of this year.

Jews who ignore this compulsory registration will be shot.

Chief of the "Einsatzgruppe"
of the "Sipo" and "SD"

Defenders of the Warsaw Ghetto are led to execution

389

390

391

Warsaw Ghetto

Arrival at the Auschwitz-Birkenau camp
SS-men select prisoners "fit for work."
All others are sent at once to the gas-chambers.

395

396

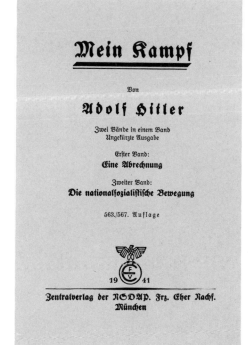

Mein Kampf

Von

Adolf Hitler

Zwei Bände in einem Band
Ungekürzte Ausgabe

Erster Band:
Eine Abrechnung

Zweiter Band:
Die nationalsozialistische Bewegung

563./567. Auflage

19 41

Zentralverlag der NSDAP. Frz. Eher Nachf.
München

397

Dem jungvermählten Paare

mit den besten Wünschen

für eine glückliche Ehe

überreicht von der

Hauptstadt der Bewegung

am 65. August 1941

Der Oberbürgermeister:

398

Hätte
man zu Kriegsbeginn und während des Krieges einmal
zwölf= oder fünfzehntausend dieser hebräischen Volksver-
derber so unter Giftgas gehalten, wie Hunderttausende
unserer allerbesten deutschen Arbeiter aus allen Schichten
und Berufen es im Felde erdulden mußten, dann wäre das
Millionenopfer der Front nicht vergeblich gewesen. Im
Gegenteil: Zwölftausend Schurken zur rechten Zeit besei-
tigt, hätte vielleicht einer Million ordentlicher, für die
Zukunft wertvoller Deutscher das Leben gerettet.

399

Hitler's "Mein Kampf", presented to all newly married couples.

"...If at the beginning and during the war someone had only subjected about 12 or 15 thousand of these destructive Hebrews to poisoned gas, as was the fate of hundreds of thousands of our best workers from all walks, of life and professions on the battlefield, then the sacrifice of millions at the front would not have been in vain. On the contrary: 12 thousand scoundrels disposed of at the right time might perhaps have saved the lives of a million decent Germans who would have been valuable for the future..."

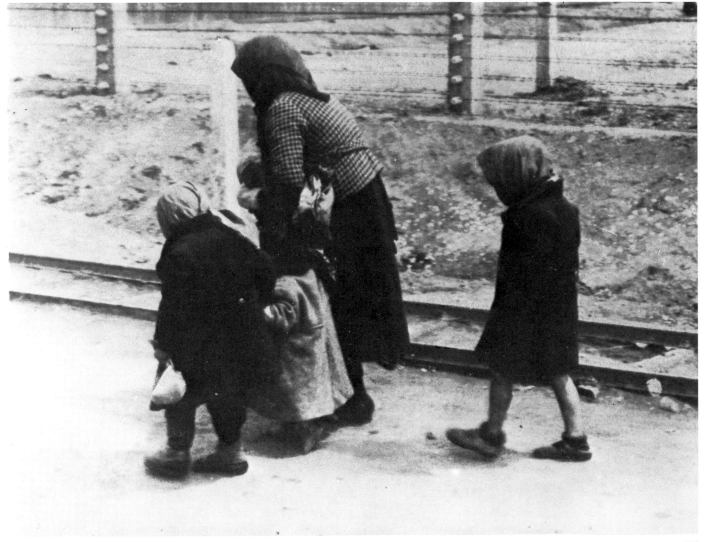

On their way to the gas-chamber

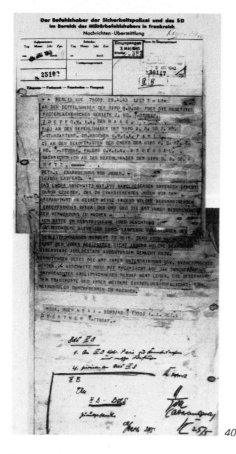

401

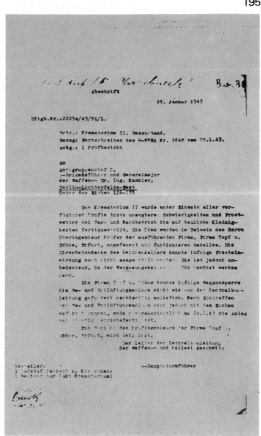

402

Reichssicherheitshauptamt
The Commander of the Security Police and the SD
in France   April 19, 1943

Teleprint to the
Commander of the Security Police and the SD
Den Hague
Paris
Brussels
Metz

Sub: Evacuation of Jews

The Auschwitz camp has requested once more that, because of obvious reasons, Jews who are to be evacuated should not be given any disturbing information before their departure regarding the impending use to which they are to be put. I request that this should be observed. I especially request that the escort commandos be constantly reminded that also during the journey no comments are to be made to the Jews or presumptions as to the nature of their accommodation etc. which could provoke resistance. Auschwitz has to carry out most urgent work projects and therefore attaches great importance to a smooth take-over and subsequent selection of the transports.

signed: Günther
SS Sturmbannführer

Copy   January 29, 1943

Subject: Crematorium II, stage of construction
Re: Teleprint from SS-WVHA, No. 2648 of Jan, 28, 1943
Encl.:   1 inspector's report

To
Amtsgruppenchef C
SS Brigadeführer and
Generalmajor of the Waffen-SS, Dr. Ing. Kammler
Berlin Lichterfelde West
Unter den Eichen 126—135

Despite unspeakable difficulties and frost, the crematorium has been completed apart from minor construction details. The whole of the available labour force was employed day and night. The incinerators were heated up in the presence of the chief engineer of Topf and Sons, contracting firm. They function perfectly. The wooden supports for the iron and concrete ceilings in the mortuary could not be removed because of frost. This is however unimportant as the gassing cellar can be used instead. Because of rail restrictions the firm Topf and Sons was not able to deliver the ventilation system punctually. As soon as the ventilation system is delivered, the installation will be started immediately so that the whole plant should be ready for service by Feb, 20, 1943. A report from the test engineer of the firm Topf and Sons, Erfurt, is enclosed.

The Chief Zentralbauleitung of the Waffen-SS
and Police Auschwitz

403
Incinerators
in Auschwitz

404
Gas-chamber
in the
Majdanek camp

405

Most of you will know what it means to be confronted with 100, 500 or 1000 corpses at one time. Having endured this experience without losing our decency—apart from occasional signs of human weakness—has hardened us. This is a glorious page of our history which never has and never will be written.

Heinrich Himmler, October 4, 1943

406   Shoes of the murdered in Auschwitz

414

415

416

417 Dachau

419

420
Dachau

421

422
Dachau-Allach

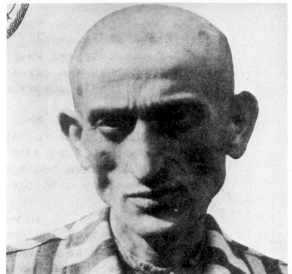

425

423

424
Dachau

426
Dachau

427
Kaufering

428

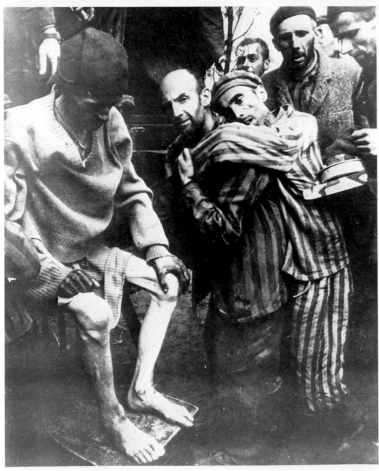

429
Buchenwald

430
Wöbbelin

Arrivals in Dachau Concentration Camp

Year	Arrivals
1933	4821
1934	1990
1935	2111
1936	2323
1937	2015
1938	18681
1939	3932
1940	22675
1941	6135
1942	12572
1943	19358
1944	78635
1945	30958

total:
206 206 prisoners

434
Registered arrivals according to the
findings of the International
Tracing Service, Arolsen.

435

436

Dachau's Dead

According to the enquiries made to date by the International Tracing Service, Arolsen,

31591 reported deaths have been ascertained for the period between 1933 and 1945.

Among the deaths whose number has not been reported and is unknown are the following:

„Sonderbehandlung" (Persons who, during the war, were assigned by the Gestapo to the Dachau concentration camp for execution)

„Kommissar-Erlaß" (Soviet prisoners of war who, by virtue of the "Kommissar-Erlaß" were executed at the Dachau concentration camp)

„Cases of deaths in evacuation transports and death marches from Dachau and subsidiary camps, March-April, 1945"

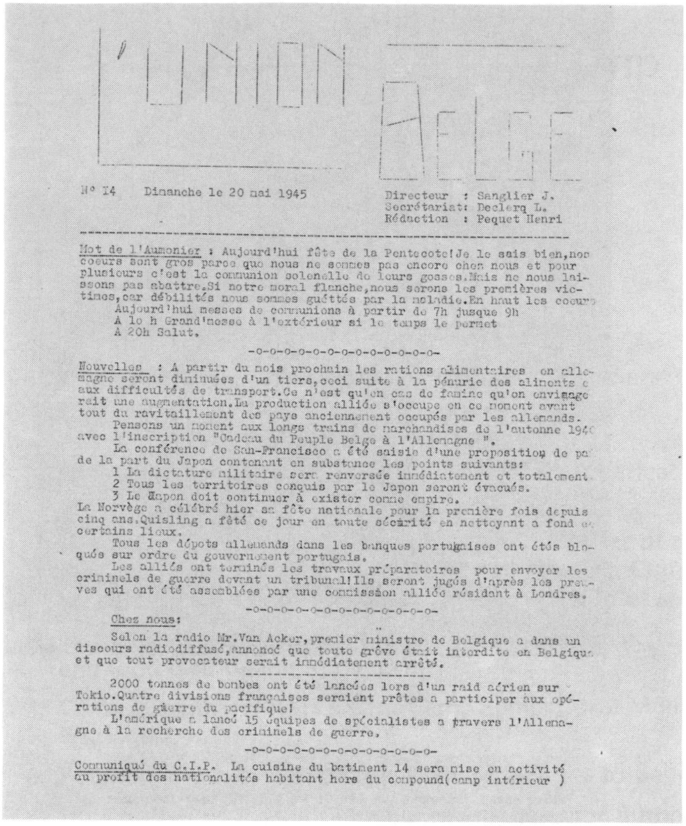

L'UNION BELGE

N° I4 Dimanche le 20 mai 1945

Directeur : Sanglier J.
Secrétariat: Declerq L.
Rédaction : Pequet Henri

Mot de l'Aumonier : Aujourd'hui fête de la Pentecote! Je le sais bien, nos coeurs sont gros parce que nous ne sommes pas encore chez nous et pour plusieurs c'est la communion solenelle de leurs gosses. Mais ne nous laissons pas abattre. Si notre moral flanche, nous serons les premières victimes, car débilités nous sommes guéttés par la maladie. En haut les coeurs
Aujourd'hui messes de communions à partir de 7h jusque 9h
A 10 h Grand'messe à l'extérieur si le temps le permet
A 20h Salut.

-o-o-o-o-o-o-o-o-o-o-o-o-o-

Nouvelles : A partir du mois prochain les rations alimentaires en allemagne seront diminuées d'un tiers, ceci suite à la pénurie des aliments e aux difficultés de transport. Ce n'est qu'en cas de famine qu'on envisagerait une augmentation. La production alliée s'occupe en ce moment avant tout du ravitaillement des pays anciennement occupés par les allemands.

Pensons un moment aux longs trains de marchandises de l'autonne 1940 avec l'inscription "Cadeau du Peuple Belge à l'Allemagne ".

La conférence de San-Francisco a été saisie d'une proposition de pa de la part du Japon contenant en substance les points suivants:
1 La dictature militaire sera renversée immédiatement et totalement
2 Tous les territoires conquis par le Japon seront évacués.
3 Le Japon doit continuer à exister comme empire.

La Norvège a célébré hier sa fête nationale pour la première fois depuis cinq ans. Quisling a fêté ce jour en toute sécurité en nettoyant a fond certains lieux.

Tous les dépots allemands dans les banques portugaises ont étés bloqués sur ordre du gouvernement portugais.

Les alliés ont terminés les travaux préparatoires pour envoyer les criminels de guerre devant un tribunal! Ils seront jugés d'après les preuves qui ont été assemblées par une commission allié résidant à Londres.

-o-o-o-o-o-o-o-o-o-o-o-o-o-

Chez nous:

Selon la radio Mr. Van Acker, premier ministre de Belgique a dans un discours radiodiffusé, annoncé que toute grève était interdite en Belgique et que tout provocateur serait immédiatement arrêté.

2000 tonnes de bombes ont été lancées lors d'un raid aérien sur Tokio. Quatre divisions françaises seraient prêtes a participer aux opérations de guerre du pacifique!

L'amérique a lancé 15 équipes de spécialistes a travers l'Allemagne à la recherche des criminels de guerre.

-o-o-o-o-o-o-o-o-o-o-o-o-o-

Communiqué du C.I.P. La cuisine du batiment 14 sera mise en activité au profit des nationalités habitant hors du compound (camp intérieur)

453

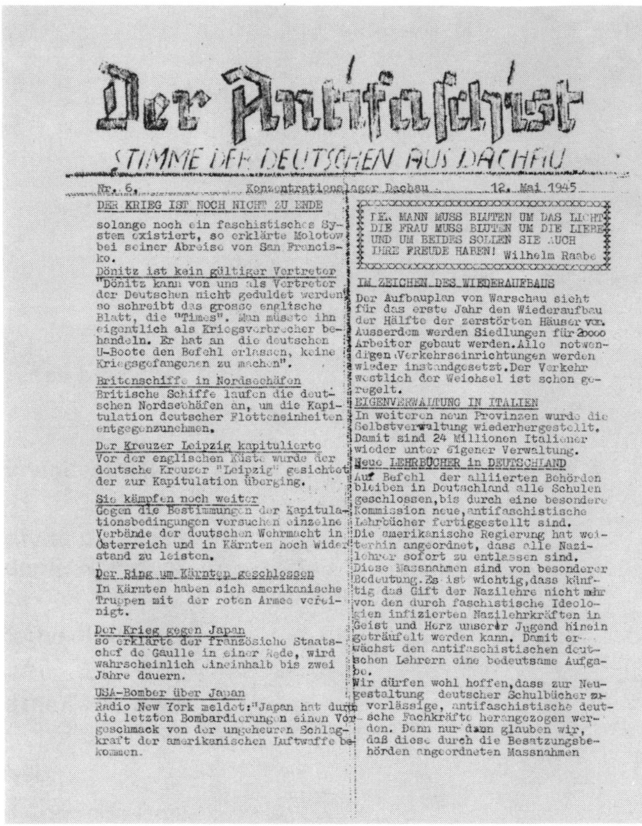

Der Antifaschist

STIMME DER DEUTSCHEN AUS DACHAU

Nr. 6. Konzentrationslager Dachau 12. Mai 1945

DER KRIEG IST NOCH NICHT ZU ENDE

solange noch ein faschistisches System existiert, so erklärte Molotow bei seiner Abreise von San Francisko.

Dönitz ist kein gültiger Vertreter

"Dönitz kann von uns als Vertreter der Deutschen nicht geduldet werden" so schreibt das grosse englische Blatt, die "Times". Man müsste ihn eigentlich als Kriegsverbrecher behandeln. Er hat an die deutschen U-Boote den Befehl erlassen, keine Kriegsgefangenen zu machen".

Britenschiffe in Nordseehäfen

Britische Schiffe laufen die deutschen Nordseehäfen an, um die Kapitulation deutscher Flotteneinheiten entgegenzunehmen.

Der Kreuzer Leipzig kapitulierte

Vor der englischen Küste wurde der deutsche Kreuzer "Leipzig" gesichtet der zur Kapitulation überging.

Sie kämpfen noch weiter

Gegen die Bestimmungen der Kapitulationsbedingungen versuchen einzelne Verbände der deutschen Wehrmacht in Österreich und in Kärnten noch Widerstand zu leisten.

Der Ring um Kärnten geschlossen

In Kärnten haben sich amerikanische Truppen mit der roten Armee vereinigt.

Der Krieg gegen Japan

so erklärte der französiche Staatschef de Gaulle in einer Rede, wird wahrscheinlich eineinhalb bis zwei Jahre dauern.

USA-Bomber über Japan

Radio New York meldet: "Japan hat durch die letzten Bombardierungen einen Vorgeschmack von der ungeheuren Schlagkraft der amerikanischen Luftwaffe bekommen.

DER MANN MUSS BLUTEN UM DAS LICHT
DIE FRAU MUSS BLUTEN UM DIE LIEBE
UND UM BEIDES SOLLEN SIE AUCH
IHRE FREUDE HABEN! Wilhelm Raabe

IM ZEICHEN DES WIEDERAUFBAUS

Der Aufbauplan von Warschau sieht für das erste Jahr den Wiederaufbau der Hälfte der zerstörten Häuser vor. Ausserdem werden Siedlungen für 20000 Arbeiter gebaut werden. Alle notwendigen Verkehrseinrichtungen werden wieder instandgesetzt. Der Verkehr westlich der Weichsel ist schon geregelt.

EIGENVERWALTUNG IN ITALIEN

In weiteren neun Provinzen wurde die Selbstverwaltung wiederhergestellt. Damit sind 24 Millionen Italiener wieder unter eigener Verwaltung.

Neue LEHRBÜCHER in DEUTSCHLAND

Auf Befehl der alliierten Behörden bleiben in Deutschland alle Schulen geschlossen, bis durch eine besondere Kommission neue, antifaschistische Lehrbücher fertiggestellt sind.
Die amerikanische Regierung hat weiterhin angeordnet, dass alle Nazilehrer sofort zu entlassen sind.
Diese Massnahmen sind von besonderer Bedeutung. Es ist wichtig, dass künftig das Gift der Nazilehre nicht mehr von den durch faschistische Ideologien infizierten Nazilehrkräften in Geist und Herz unserer Jugend hineingeträufelt werden kann. Damit erwächst den antifaschistischen deutschen Lehrern eine bedeutsame Aufgabe.
Wir dürfen wohl hoffen, dass zur Neugestaltung deutscher Schulbücher zuverlässige, antifaschistische deutsche Fachkräfte herangezogen werden. Denn nur dann glauben wir, daß diese durch die Besatzungsbehörden angeordneten Massnahmen

455

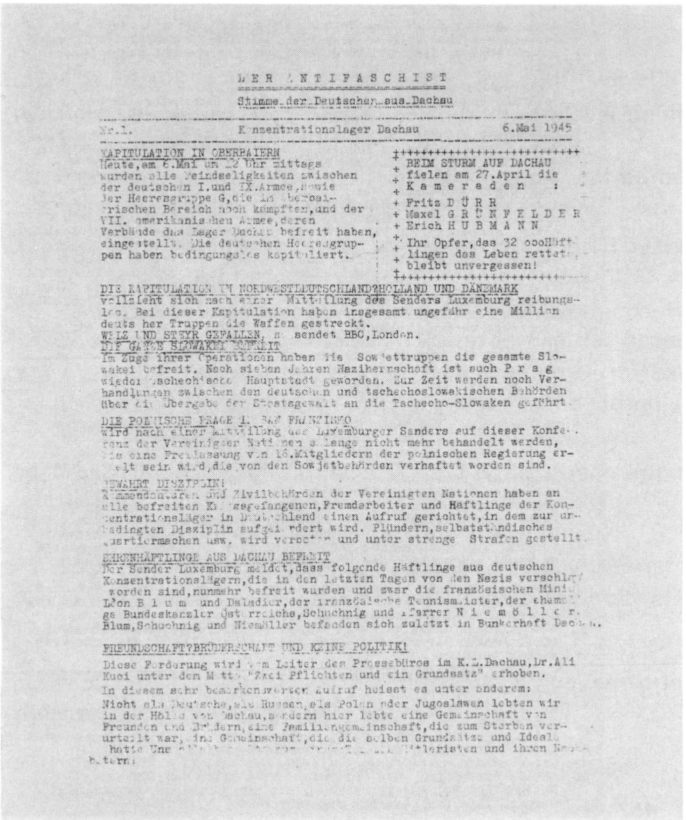

DER ANTIFASCHIST

Stimme der Deutschen aus Dachau

Nr. 1. Konzentrationslager Dachau 6. Mai 1945

KAPITULATION IN OBERBAIERN

Heute, am 6. Mai um 12 Uhr mittags wurden alle Feindseligkeiten zwischen der deutschen I. und IX. Armee, sowie der Heeresgruppe G, die im oberbaierischen Bereich noch kämpften, und der VII. amerikanischen Armee, deren Verbände das Lager Dachau befreit haben, eingestellt. Die deutschen Heeresgruppen haben bedingungslos kapituliert.

BEIM STURM AUF DACHAU fielen am 27. April die Kameraden:
Fritz DÜRR
Maxel GRÜNFELDER
Erich HUBMANN
Ihr Opfer, das 32 000 Häftlingen das Leben rettete, bleibt unvergessen!

DIE KAPITULATION IN NORDWESTDEUTSCHLAND?HOLLAND UND DÄNEMARK

vollzieht sich nach einer Mitteilung des Senders Luxemburg reibungslos. Bei dieser Kapitulation haben insgesamt ungefähr eine Million deutscher Truppen die Waffen gestreckt.

WELZ UND STEYR GEFALLEN, so sendet BBC, London.

DIE GANZE SLOWAKEI BEFREIT

Im Zuge ihrer Operationen haben die Sowjettruppen die gesamte Slowakei befreit. Nach sieben Jahren Naziherrschaft ist auch Prag wieder tschechische Hauptstadt geworden. Zur Zeit werden noch Verhandlungen zwischen den deutschen und tschechoslowakischen Behörden über die Übergabe der Staatsgewalt an die Tschecho-Slowaken geführt.

DIE POLNISCHE FRAGE IN SAN FRANZISKO

wird nach einer Mitteilung des Luxemburger Senders auf dieser Konferenz der Vereinigten Nationen solange nicht mehr behandelt werden, bis eine Freilassung von 16. Mitgliedern der polnischen Regierung erzielt sein wird, die von den Sowjetbehörden verhaftet worden sind.

BEWAHRT DISZIPLIN!

Kommandanturen und Zivilbehörden der Vereinigten Nationen haben an alle befreiten Kriegsgefangenen, Fremdarbeiter und Häftlinge der Konzentrationsläger in Deutschland einen Aufruf gerichtet, in dem zur unbedingten Disziplin aufgefordert wird. Plündern, selbstständisches Quartiermachen usw. wird verboten und unter strenge Strafen gestellt.

EHRENHÄFTLINGE AUS DACHAU BEFREIT

Der Sender Luxemburg meldet, dass folgende Häftlinge aus deutschen Konzentrationslägern, die in den letzten Tagen von den Nazis verschleppt worden sind, nunmehr befreit wurden und zwar die französischen Minister Léon Blum und Daladier, der französische Tennismeister, der ehemalige Bundeskanzler Österreichs, Schuschnig und Pfarrer Niemöller. Blum, Schuschnig und Niemöller befanden sich zuletzt in Bunkerhaft Dachau.

FREUNDSCHAFT?BRÜDERSCHAFT UND KEINE POLITIK!

Diese Forderung wird vom Leiter des Pressebüros im K.L. Dachau, Dr. Ali Kuci unter dem Motto "Zwei Pflichten und ein Grundsatz" erhoben.

In diesem sehr bemerkenswerten Aufruf heisst es unter anderem:

Nicht als Deutsche, als Russen, als Polen oder Jugoslawen lebten wir in der Hölle von Dachau, sondern hier lebte eine Gemeinschaft von Freunden und Brüdern, eine Familiengemeinschaft, die zum Sterben verurteilt war, eine Gemeinschaft, die die selben Grundsätze und Ideale hatte Uns ... Hitleristen und ihren Henkern:

454

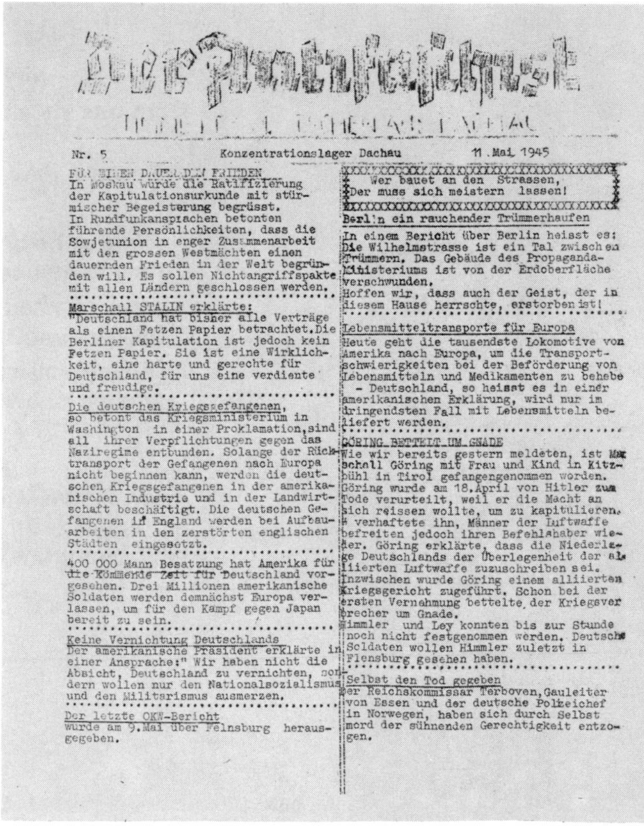

Der Antifaschist

Nr. 5 Konzentrationslager Dachau 11. Mai 1945

FÜR EINEN DAUERNDEN FRIEDEN

In Moskau würde die Ratifizierung der Kapitulationsurkunde mit stürmischer Begeisterung begrüsst.
In Rundfunkansprachen betonten führende Persönlichkeiten, dass die Sowjetunion in enger Zusammenarbeit mit den grossen Westmächten einen dauernden Frieden in der Welt begründen will. Es sollen Nichtangriffspakte mit allen Ländern geschlossen werden.

Marschall STALIN erklärte:

"Deutschland hat bisher alle Verträge als einen Fetzen Papier betrachtet. Die Berliner Kapitulation ist jedoch kein Fetzen Papier. Sie ist eine Wirklichkeit, eine harte und gerechte für Deutschland, für uns eine verdiente und freudige.

Die deutschen Kriegsgefangenen,

so betont das Kriegsministerium in Washington in einer Proklamation, sind all ihrer Verpflichtungen gegen das Naziregime entbunden. Solange der Rücktransport der Gefangenen nach Europa nicht beginnen kann, werden die deutschen Kriegsgefangenen in der amerikanischen Industrie und in der Landwirtschaft beschäftigt. Die deutschen Gefangenen in England werden bei Aufbauarbeiten in den zerstörten englischen Städten eingesetzt.

400 000 Mann Besatzung hat Amerika für die kommende Zeit für Deutschland vorgesehen. Drei Millionen amerikanische Soldaten werden demnächst Europa verlassen, um für den Kampf gegen Japan bereit zu sein.

Keine Vernichtung Deutschlands

Der amerikanische Präsident erklärte in einer Ansprache:" Wir haben nicht die Absicht, Deutschland zu vernichten, sondern wollen nur den Nationalsozialismus und den Militarismus ausmerzen.

Der letzte OKW-Bericht

wurde am 9. Mai über Felnsburg herausgegeben.

Wer bauet an den Strassen,
Der muss sich meistern lassen!

Berlin ein rauchender Trümmerhaufen

In einem Bericht über Berlin heisst es: Die Wilhelmstrasse ist ein Tal zwischen Trümmern. Das Gebäude des Propaganda-Ministeriums ist von der Erdoberfläche verschwunden.
Hoffen wir, dass auch der Geist, der in diesem Hause herrschte, erstorben ist!

Lebensmitteltransporte für Europa

Heute geht die tausendste Lokomotive von Amerika nach Europa, um die Transportschwierigkeiten bei der Beförderung von Lebensmitteln und Medikamenten zu behebe
- Deutschland, so heisst es in einer amerikanischen Erklärung, wird nur im dringendsten Fall mit Lebensmitteln beliefert werden.

GÖRING BETTELT UM GNADE

Wie wir bereits gestern meldeten, ist Marschall Göring mit Frau und Kind in Kitzbühl in Tirol gefangengenommen worden. Göring wurde am 18. April von Hitler zum Tode verurteilt, weil er die Macht an sich reissen wollte, um zu kapitulieren. SS verhaftete ihn, Männer der Luftwaffe befreiten jedoch ihren Befehlshaber wieder. Göring erklärte, dass die Niederlage Deutschlands der Überlegenheit der alliierten Luftwaffe zuzuschreiben sei. Inzwischen wurde Göring einem alliierten Kriegsgericht zugeführt. Schon bei der ersten Vernehmung bettelte der Kriegsverbrecher um Gnade.
Himmler und Ley konnten bis zur Stunde noch nicht festgenommen werden. Deutsche Soldaten wollen Himmler zuletzt in Flensburg gesehen haben.

Selbst den Tod gegeben

Der Reichskommissar Terboven, Gauleiter von Essen und der deutsche Polizeichef in Norwegen, haben sich durch Selbstmord der sühnenden Gerechtigkeit entzogen.

456

457

COMITE FRANCAIS

(Bulletin quotidien d'Informations)

Numéro 6   Dachau, 7 mai 1945

-- LES RUSSES P... MOTENT

DES TROUPES PRES DE PRAGUE

Hier, les allemands, après avoir déclaré une trêve avec les Patriotes Tchèques, revenaient sur le prol.. donné. A 11 H.... ils rapprenaient leur rmes. Les Russes prenaient des troupes et du matériel au nord de la ville. Patton est à 55 kms au S. de Pilsen, les blindés sont à moins de 80 kms de Prague.

Les Américains sont entrés d'Linz tandisque leurs avancés pénètraient dans Berchtesgaden.

.... Himmler, lui aussi, ... été parachuté à Copenhague où ils dérament les Allemands qui se sont rendus. Le Général Allemand commandant les troupes de Norvège à offert sa reddition. Elle a été refusée.

Les Américains progressent dans l'île de Mindanao.

LECLERC DORMIT AU LIT D'HITLER

Ce sont les troupes françaises du Général Leclerc qui ont occupé Berchtesgaden, résidence favorite d'Hitler.

Des officiers de la division venus hier visiter le camp nous ont donné une amusante précision: Le Général Leclerc à dormi dans le lit d'Hitler.

Mais, ont-ils précisé, on avait changé les draps.....'

LEON BLUM ET JOUHAUX LIBRES

... Léon Blum, dont le sort semblait critique depuis son passage à Dachau, a été libéré par les troupes américaines, ainsi que Léon Jouhaux, secrétaire général de la C.G.T.

Communications officielles du camp

BIBLIOTHEQUE, CINEMA, TABAC

MIS A NOTRE DISPOSITION

1.- Le Comité International a été informé par le commandant du camp qu'une partie des baraques S.S. qui se trouvent hors du camp pourraient être mises à notre disposition pour les malades. Leur nombre n'excèdera pas 3.000. Les autres baraques ne sont pas disponibles parce-qu'on a trouvé des mines sous les fondements. Le .... précisé que le Comité chargé de la distribution du logement était chargé de trouver un autre local. Dès qu'il l'aura, il le fera savoir.

2.- L'Officier de l'armée américaine, chargé de l'intendance du camp a informé le Comité que chaque jour la ration de pain et de nourriture était accrue en qualité et en quantité.

3.- Le Comité a décidé d'organiser le plus rapidement possible des distractions pour les prisonniers. Dès jours-ci la bibliothèque sera ouverte et un cinéma installé. La question des appareils de radio résolue de manière que dans tous les blocs autant que possible, il y ait la radio.

4.- Du tabac et des cigarettes vont être fournis pour tout le camp.

5.- Le Commandant a informé le Comité que l'évacuation du camp sera effectuée comme suit: dès que les malades auront été soignés des bien portants, il y aura une désinfection pendant 14 jours après, s'il n'y a plus aucun cas de typhus, l'évacuation commencera aussitôt.

6.- Il est arrivé au camp un corps sanitaire des infirmières de la croix Rouge américaine. Elles concourent par tous les moyens à améliorer la santé des prisonniers et leur rendent toutes sortes de services.

458

17 18 ΙΟΥΝΙΟΥ 1945

ΑΡΙΘΜ. ΦΥΛΛΟΥ 9   ΕΚΔΙΔΕΤΑΙ ΑΠΑΞ ΤΗΣ ΕΒΔΟΜΑΔΟΣ

Η ΕΛΕΥΘΕΡΑ ΔΩΔΕΚΑΝΗΣΟΣ

ΕΦΗΜΕΡΙΣ ΤΩΝ ΕΝ ΝΤΑΧΑΟΥ ΕΛΛΗΝΩΝ ≈ ΥΠΕΥΘΥΝΟΣ ΘΑΝΑΣ ΕΜΜ. ΣΠΥΡΟΥ

ΕΦΘΑΣΕ ΣΤΗΝ ΠΑΤΡΙΔΑ....

[handwritten article, largely illegible]

Διευθ.

Giovanni Melodia

459

.R.   Vorderdag, 10 Mei 1945

"DE STEM DER LAGE LANDEN"

Orgaan der Nederlanders te Dachau

Nederl. Vertrouwensman: Redactie:
Willem Boellaard   Ed Hoernik,
Secr. Nat. Comité: Nico Rost,
Rob Cox; Postoffice.   Marc v.Hasselt

BELGIE - NEDERLAND - LUXEMBURG

1940 - 10 MEI - 1945.

Vandaag, 10 Mei, herdenken België, Nederland en Luxemburg het feit, dat vijf jaar geleden de Duitsche legers deze drie landen binnenvielen. Hieronder geven wij het woord aan een Belg, een Nederlander en een Luxemburger, die ieder op zijn manier een terugblik houdt en toekomstperspectieven opent. -

Een Belg schrijft ons.

10 Mei 1940. - Na 25 jaren vrede trokken de Duitsche horden opnieuw ... land binnen, welke onschendbaarheid zij zoo even nog plechtig gewaarborgd. De mannen van het Albert-kanaal weerstaan moedig dun stoot ... begint de heldhaftige campagne der 18 dagen in den loop waarvan onze soldaten, in weerwil van de flagrante minderheid, voet voor voet ons grondgebied verdedigen. In dien ongelijken strijd wordt België's ... opnieuw gedrenkt met het bloed zijner zonen.

10 Mei 1945. - De bevrijde gevangenen van Dachau herinneren zich hun strijders van het Albert-kanaal, van de fortjes en fortun in de Ardennen, van de dans om 't bezit van de oevers der Leie. Zij herinneren zich de heldhaftige strijders van Mei 1940 wier bloedig offer vindelijk werd beloond; zij herinneren zich ook hun gevangen makkers die nog talrijker vielen dan hun wapenbroeders, en wier dood niet minder heldhaftig was. Zij zijn gevallen onder dun last van typhus, van honger, van de werkdagen onder hun last van honger, van de werkdagen van hun beulen hun dood ondergaan in de uitroeiingskampen. Vrienden in Dachau, laten wij, vorderd door de vijandelijk verworven vrijheid, onze dooden niet vergeten, maar tonen wij ons hun gedachtenis waardig door vergengd te blijven in dezelfde liefde voor het Vaderland, in dezelfde liefde voor de menschen. Moken wij het offer van ons nuttloos leven door solidarisch onze persoonlijk belangen op den voorgrond te schuiven. Komen wij in den geest van zelfverloochening en zelfopoffering de beproevingen aan die ons nog scheiden van de definitieve vrijheid, zoodoende zullen wij de meest solide grondslagen voor een waarlijk hechten vrede.

Een Nederlander schrijft ons:

In tweeërlei opzicht zal de dag van heden voor België, Luxemburg en Nederland steeds een datum van historische beteekenis blijven, die de volkeren dezer kleine staten voor altijd zal verbinden. Eenerzds rukt ... dien nacht de horden der nazi's ons landen binnen om onder de brute wieg vijf jaar lang dood en verdurf te zaaien. In de tweede plaats was het dien dag het uitgangspunt van het moedig en onwankelbaar verzet ... der volken, om aan het ...ormende fascisme weerstand te bieden, waar dit slechts mogelijk was. Dit gezamelijk verzet van drie staten, dik anders steeds hun eigen weg vervolgden, zal hen in de toekomst nog vaster aaneensmeden. Omtrent dit verzet was van te voren niets afge...

460

n. 32   DIR. GIOVANNI MELODIA   16/5/1945

- Problemi di domani -

IMPEDIRE UN NUOVO " SQUADRISMO "

Tutti sanno che uno degli aspetti morali della dittatura veramente fu il fenomeno o diciamo meglio, la piaga sempre purulenta dello squadrismo. Tutte le cariche dello Stato, grandi e piccole che fossero, furono trasformate in un monopolio squadrista. E ci fu dato così di vedere avvilendi ministri e sottosegretari, consiglieri nazionali, direttori di giornali, che erano delle autentiche nullità ma che, in cambio, possedevano il crisma della marcia su Roma e quel che sembrerebbe impossibile se non fosse stradocumentato, lo stesso criterio valse per posti richiedenti alte competenze tecniche ed amministrative e perfino grandi benemerenze scientifiche (vedi il caso dei rettori di Università) qualsicché tutti gli imbecilli che erano stati squadristi avessero avuto in dono al de Dominedio le dotti non certo comuni che si richiedono a coloro che tengono in pugno i gangli vitali e la complessa e multiforme attività di una moderna nazione.

Ma quanto avveniva al centro non mancava di ripetersi in scala anche più ampia in provincia: una miriade di gerarchi, gerarchetti e gerarchetti, presuntuosi quanto ignoranti, saccenti quanto incompetenti, annidati negli uffici più vari e nelle cariche più delicate e di null'altro capaci di sfoggiare aquile dorate facendo un contegno gli occhiacci terribili a simiglianza del capo, furono i più coscienziosi diaggregatori della compagine statale e dello stesso regime che li sosteneva.

Il solo ricordare tutto ciò ci fa nausea cosi profonda che il pensiero che qualcosa di analogo possa egualmente verificarsi domani, ci è causa di una profonda preoccupazione.

Ci saranno anche domani gli arrivisti, gli assaltatori di cariche pubbliche in base a ipotetici meriti precedenti? Ebbene, essi devono essere inesorabilmente stroncati al loro nascere.

L'aver duramente e valorosamente combattuto, i sacrifici, i dolori, le privazioni, la persecuzione, sono altrettanti titoli di alto onore per color che possono vantarli e la riconoscenza della Patria sarà eterna. Ma non vi è in basa a benemerenze militari ed ad atti di eroismo che si possono affidare a degli uomini cariche che comportano una somma di responsabilità e che esigono conoscenze e competenze tecniche specifiche non facilmente acquisibili. E'il benessere e la tranquillità della popolazione; è la stessa vita politica, economica ed amministrativa della nazione, che dipendono e che non devono essere messi nuovamente in giuoco.

Altro è guida un battaglione d'assalto, altro dirigere oculatamente un ufficio di interesse pubblico. E soprattutto, osserviamo dire, esclusivamente sulla probità, sulla rettitudine, sulle capacità intellettuali e morali degli individui che ci dovremmo basare, e non già sui meriti acquistati in campi tutt'affatto diversi.

★ SMRT FAŠIZMU • SVOBODA NARODU!

DAHAVSKI P JROČEVALEC

GLASILO JUGOSLOVANSKEGA NARODNEGA ODBORA

Štev. 10 — Dachau, dne 12. maja 1945 — Broj 10

IZ PRAZNIČNEGA ZANOSA – V DELAVNI DAN

Prva vlada suverene demokratične Slovenije • Naša prestolnica je začela novo življenje

461

DAS NEUE

ÖSTERREICH

No. 3   MITTEILUNGSBLATT DER ÖSTERREICHER IN DACHAU , Juni 1945

Aus Anlass der Wiederinbetriebsetzung des Wiener Senders fand im Gebäude der RAVAG eine offizielle Feier statt, bei der die Minister-präs. Dr. Renner im Namen der Österreichischen Regierung, Staats-sekr. Schärf im Namen der soz. Partei, Staatssekr. Figel im Namen der Volkspart. und Staatssekr. Koplenig im Namen der kommun. Partei an das österreichische Volk, an die Alliierten und an alle freiheit-liebenden Völker der Welt eine Ansprache hielten.

Die einzelnen Reden wurden in franz., russ., und engl. Sprache wieder-gegeben. Im Nachstehenden Auszüge aus den Reden der einzelnen Ver-treter der Regierung :

MINISTERPRÄS. Dr. RENNER führte aus :

462

NR.4   SOBOTA 12.V.

GŁOS POLSKI
1945
Organ Komitetu Polskiego w Dachau

W DNIU ZWYCIĘSTWA

POLSKA JESZCZE NIE JEST ZWOLNIONA

NOWI LUDZIE W NOWYCH CZASACH

463

Those who cannot remember
the past
are condemned to repeat it.

Santayana

464

228

SOURCES:

Nr.:

1-4 Dachau-Archiv
5 Stuttgart (Frommans), 1922
6 München (Bruckmann), 1922
7 Balluseck, Frei sein wie die Väter Bad Godesberg (Hohwacht), 1960
8 Leipzig (Kröner), 1934
9 Leipzig (T. Fritsch), 1909
10 Leipzig (Hammer, T. Fritsch), 1919
11 Leipzig (Hammer), 1929
12-14 Daim, W., Der Mann, der Hitler die Ideen gab, München (Isar), 1958
15 Dachau-Archiv
16 Bamberg (C.C. Buchners), 1911
17 Grebing, H., Der Nationalsozialismus, München (Olzog), 1964
18 Arnold, F., Anschläge Ebenhausen (Langewiesche-Brandt), 1963
19-20 Huber, H., Müller, A., Das Dritte Reich Band I, München (Desch), 1964
21 Arnold, F., s.o.
22 Huber, H., s.o.
23 Hofer, W., Der Nationalsozialismus Frankfurt/M. (Fischer), 1957
24-26 Arnold, F., s.o.
27-28 Ullstein Bildarchiv
29 Huber, H., s.o.
30 Arnold, F., s.o.
31 Keystone Bildarchiv
32 Arnold, F., s.o.
33 Copress Bildverlag
34 Münchner Neueste Nachrichten 2.4.1924
35 Pross, H., Die Zerstörung der deutschen Politik 1871—1933 Frankfurt/M. (Fischer), 1959
36 Jasper, G., Aus den Akten der Prozesse gegen die Erzbergermörder Stuttgart (Kohlhammer, VfZ 4/62) 1962
37 Arnold, F., s.o.
38-39 Von Heimat und Vaterland, Band III, Kaiserslautern, 1926
40-41 Huber, H., s.o.
42 Münchner Neueste Nachrichten 26.9.1930
43-44 Arnold, F., s.o.
45 Copress Bildverlag
46-48 London (Holder & Stoughton, Ltd.) 1941
49 Neumann, R., Hitler München (Desch), 1961
50 Keystone Bildarchiv
51 Arnold, F., s.o.
52 A. Paul Weber, Hamburg
53 Deutschland erwacht, Altona-Behrenfeld (Zigaretten-Bilderdienst), 1933
54 Huber, H., s.o.
55 Arnold, F., s.o.

56 Neumann, R., s.o.
57 Arnold, F., s.o.
58 Krummacher, F., Wucher, A., Die Weimarer Republik 1918—1933 München (Desch), 1965
59 Dachau-Archiv
60 Heine, H., Almansor, Trauerspiel 1820/21
61 Copress Bildverlag
62 Reichsgesetzblatt Teil 1/Nr. 17 vom 28.2.1933
63 Völkischer Beobachter, 11./12.3.1933
64 Völkischer Beobachter, 15.3.1933
65 Völkischer Beobachter, 11./12.3.1933
66 Amper-Bote 12./13.3.1933
67** Museum für Deutsche Geschichte, Berlin
68* Kongress Verlag, Berlin
69 Dachau-Archiv
70 Berliner Tageblatt, 2.12.1935
71 Der Stürmer, Sondernr., 1.5.1934
72 Berliner Tageblatt, 18.5.1934
73* Landesbildstelle, Berlin
74 Dachau-Archiv
75 Illustrierter Beobachter, Folge 49/1936
76 Süddeutscher Verlag, Bilderdienst
77 Zentrale Stelle der Landesjustizverwaltungen, Ludwigsburg
78-79 Staatsarchiv, Nürnberg
80-81 Dachau-Archiv
82 Völkischer Beobachter, 21.3.1933
83 Münchner Neueste Nachrichten, 21.3.1933
84 Münchner Neueste Nachrichten, 23.3.1933
85 Amper-Bote, 7.9.1933
86 Amper-Bote, 14./15.4.1933
87 Amper-Bote, 2.6.1933
88 Münchner Illustrierte Presse, 16.7.1933
89-90 Dachau-Archiv
91-92 Instytut Slaski, Opole
93-94 Dachau-Archiv
95 Instytut Slaski, Opole
96-101 Dachau-Archiv
102 Schnabel, R., Macht ohne Moral Frankfurt/M. (Röderberg), 1957
103-104 Dachau-Archiv
105 Schnabel, R., s.o.
106 Dachau-Archiv
107 Amper-Bote, 9.12.1933
108 Dachau-Archiv
109 Staatsarchiv Nürnberg
110-111 International Tracing Service, Arolsen
112 Zentrale Stelle, s.o.
113 Domagala, J., Die durch Dachau gingen, Warschau (Pax), 1957

114 Alzin, J., Father Titus Brandsma Dublin (Clonmore & Reynolds Ltd), 1957
115 Bundesarchiv Koblenz
116-117 Staatsarchiv Nürnberg
118 Dachau-Archiv
119-122 Zentrale Stelle, s.o.
123 Dachau-Archiv
124 Yad Vashem Jerusalem
125 Rijksinstituut voor Oorlogsdocumentatie, Amsterdam
126 Keystone Bildarchiv
127 Dachau-Archiv
128-129 Zentrale Stelle, s.o.
130 Rijksinstituut, s.o.
131 Dachau-Archiv
132 US Army Photograph
133 Rijksinstituut, s.o.
134 US Army Pictoral Center, Long Island
135-136 Staatsarchiv Nürnberg
137 Dachau-Archiv
138 Staatsarchiv Nürnberg
139 Kogon, E., Der SS-Staat Frankfurt/M. (Europäische Verlagsanstalt), 1946
140 Rijksinstituut, s.o.
141 Illustrierter Beobachter, Folge 49/1936
142-144 Dachau-Archiv
145 Zentrale Stelle, s.o.
146 Bundesarchiv Koblenz
147 Illustrierter Beobachter, Folge 49/1936
148 Yad Vashem Jerusalem
149** Imperial War Museum, London
150-151 Dachau-Archiv
152-154 Nationalsozialistische Monatshefte Heft 46/Januar 1934
155 Wucher, A., Eichmanns gab es viele München (Droemer), 1961
156 Staatsarchiv Nürnberg
157-161 Rijksinstituut, s.o.
162 Dachau-Archiv
163 US Army Photograph
164 Dachau-Archiv
165 Glonntal-Bote, 1./2./3.IV.1934
166 Amper-Bote, 14./15.1.1934
167 Illustrierter Beobachter, Folge 49/1936
168 Münchner Illustrierte Presse 16.7.1933
169 Illustrierter Beobachter, Folge 49/1936
170 Arbeiter Zeitung, Wien 4.1.1934
171 Karlsbad (Graphia), 1934
172 London (Modern Books Ltd), o.J.
173 Moskau-Leningrad (Verlagsgenossenschaft ausländischer Arbeiter in der UdSSR), 1933